May Day procession in the Red Square Moscow 1920

ART IN

REVOLUTION

Soviet Art and Design since 1917
Hayward Gallery London
26 February to 18 April 1971

Arts Council

Catalogue designed by
Brian Dunce

Printed by
Shenval Press

Contents

Preface

This exhibition meets a specific need. The names of two or three Soviet artists of the Revolutionary period have become familiar in recent years, partly through books and articles, partly through exhibitions, but the many achievements of Soviet art and design in the 1920s remain unknown to all but a few specialists. Recent histories of art by eminent scholars bear witness to this fact in perpetuating it.

Yet the years following the 1917 Revolution saw a most remarkable phase in modern art. Avant-garde artists were placed in commanding positions, academic conservatism was temporarily silenced, and the arts joined with political forces in an attempt to build an egalitarian world on the double basis of modern technology and socialism.

It is the mingling of artistic and social drives, and thus the abandonment of fine art's segregation from everyday life, that gives this phase its unique character and value. The exhibition has been designed to reflect this. It stresses the influence of various art forms upon each other and illustrates the concurrent work in fields normally kept separate of the same creative men and women. And it places their work against the background of contemporary life in a manner which in itself is intended to reflect the period.

Its effect must necessarily be impressionistic. A great deal of research is still to be done before the detailed account of post-Revolutionary art and design can be written. In addition, it is not yet possible to bring together all the apposite material that is known to exist. We have intentionally made the exhibition kaleidoscopic rather than piecemeal and we have resisted the temptation to make it encyclopaedic. We considered its total impact, and the impact of each of its sections, as much as the significance of any particular item.

The proposal for this exhibition came some years ago from Camilla Gray-Prokofieva. That it has been realised is very largely due to her efforts. We were glad to obtain the collaboration of the Ministry of Culture of the USSR, and we thank the Ministry and the specialist appointed to supervise its contribution, Mr Shvidkovsky, for the loan of works of art, theatre models and a great amount of documentary material, including that in the special section of Soviet design since 1930. It is clear that Soviet architecture has recently developed quite remarkably and that this development is international in character. We are grateful to the lenders who have added important items from private and public collections. Mr Shvidkovsky, and his colleague in the Moscow Institute of Art History, Mr Khan-Mahomedov, have contributed useful and informative articles to this book. We have been glad of the help of Mr V Karyagin of the Soviet Embassy, and also of our cultural attaché in Moscow, John Field.

The articles that follow reveal also some of the other creators of this exhibition: Edward Braun, expert on the Russian theatre, whose involvement extended far beyond his special subject; Lutz Becker, the film maker, who contributed the documentary film in the first gallery and the splendid photomontages in the third and fourth, and made excellent suggestions affecting the general appearance of the exhibition; and Edward Wright who did the graphics, which means the banners, the flag, the button and much else.

Michael Brawne designed the installation but also brought his specialist knowledge and a marked enthusiasm to the architectural display and to the crucial matter of model making. The several people who made the reconstructions for us are credited in the catalogue; here it should be stated that the tasks we set them were exceptionally difficult and that their success proves an involvement beyond the normal call of duty. We are very glad to be allowed to print a largely rewritten version of Kenneth Frampton's important article of 1968 on 'The Lost Avant-Garde'.

The exhibition would have been incomplete without a section showing Soviet documentary and feature films of the period. An ideal solution to this problem was found, and we are most grateful for this to Sir William Coldstream and to Stanley Reed of the British Film Institute, and to Leslie Hardcastle and Ken Wlaschin of the National Film Theatre. The film programmes that have resulted from their co-operation are outlined at the back of this book.

ROBIN CAMPBELL
director of art

NORBERT LYNTON
director of exhibitions

Introduction
Camilla Gray-Prokofieva

This exhibition was conceived several years ago as an attempt to define one of the most important of modern art movements – Constructivism. We felt that this had become a much-cited name but although Constructivism was recognised as a major contribution to twentieth-century art history, only a vague idea existed as to what this term actually meant. Although cited so often and so enthusiastically, particularly in the last ten years, contradictory and historically false ideas have become increasingly associated with it. For example, it is often to be read in recent Western European and American publications that Gabo and his brother Anton Pevsner were founder-members of the Constructivist movement and their 'Realistic Manifesto', signed and posted up in the streets of Moscow in 1920, is treated as a central Constructivist statement. In fact this declaration, as Gabo explains in his note to his English translation, was produced as a riposte to the recently published statement of the Productivist group. This Productivist group of artists within a couple of years came to adopt the term Constructivism to cover their aims and ideas. The precise origin of the name and its first use by these artists has not yet been established, but from 1920 onwards one finds it being used more and more in statements by this group, headed by Tatlin.

This exhibition thus covers all the various fields in which Constructivist ideas were developed: in the theatre by Meyerhold, in architecture by the Vesnin brothers, Leonidov and the OSA group, in cinema by Dziga Vertov, in industrial, theatrical and typographical design by Rodchenko, Stepanova, Popova, and again in exhibition and poster design by Klutsis, Lissitzky and the Stenberg brothers.

In 1922 Tarabukin's booklet *Constructivism* was published which one may regard as the first of the primary statements of this movement. Declarations by the other principal theoreticians

Agit-train 1919

of this group – Osip Brik and Arvatov – are chiefly to be found in the central Constructivist magazine *Lef* (which ran from 1923–25 and under the title *Novy Lef* from 1927–28), edited by the poets Mayakovsky and Tretyakov. Excerpts from these statements are included in this catalogue; in shorter form we have introduced them in the form of slogans in the exhibition – slogans being the typical form that many of these statements originally took. As far as possible we have tried to retain in the exhibition the graphic style and techniques of the period as we felt that these convey in themselves so much of the turbulent, heroic, revolutionary time which gave them life. Indeed we consider that a cold, rational treatment of our theme would not convey the ideas with which we are dealing. The fact that it is ideas, primarily, that the Constructivists contributed to the modern movement makes their presentation in an exhibition a problem and a challenge.

We have tried to answer the challenge by treating the subject on several levels – as a spectacle to be enjoyed, as a re-creation of history on a social and historical level and as a chapter of art history.

We have included a good deal of material not strictly or only marginally Constructivist. For, when we finally came to consider the selection of material, we realised that in works actually created, only a few could qualify as entirely expressing Constructivist ideas. Others bear certain characteristics only. For example, the Tairov production of Chesterton's *Man who was Thursday* was not Constructivist although the architectural set by Alexander Vesnin was entirely so; again, the posters by the Stenberg brothers are Constructivist in technique but very seldom in content.

To make clear what Constructivism is really about, we have given prominence to the primary examples such as *The Magnanimous Cuckold*, the Meyerhold-Popova theatrical production of 1922, the *Leningrad Pravda* design of Alexander Vesnin and his brothers of 1924, the poster and photomontage work of Gustav Klutsis, a Constructivist graphic designer of primary importance although hardly heard of in the West. Finally as a symbol of the utopian vision of these artists we have reconstructed the model of the *Tower-Monument to the Third International* of 1919–1920 by Vladimir Tatlin. Sadly we have not been able to show in the actual exhibition galleries the *Kino-Pravda* (Cinema-Truth) pioneer newsreel series of Dziga Vertov, so much part of the Constructivist movement. However, the British Film Institute, co-operating with the Arts Council, has arranged a daily showing of *Kino-Pravda* throughout the duration of this exhibition.

In order to give the British public of 1971 an idea of the world of Russia of 1917 which gave rise to Constructivism, we have in the first room a compilation film of contemporary Russian newsreels. We felt that this social, historical backcloth of revolution was essential as an introduction to our theme. Further on the visitor will find 'street art': mass-spectacles performed in public squares, designs for tribines to be set up at street corners from which to inform the public about the new social order, designs for monuments to the new revolutionary heroes (a project inspired by Lenin), designs for the streets and buildings to celebrate the new public holidays. For in Mayakovsky's words: 'Let us make the streets our brushes, the squares our palette.' This immediate post-Revolutionary involvement by these artists was the stepping-stone from their 'ivory tower' activities of easel painting, private architecture and theatre, to an involvement in everyday life, an involvement which led directly to the creation of Constructivism.

Of the fine art roots of Constructivism, Vladimir Tatlin's *Reliefs* and *Counter Reliefs* which date from the winter of 1913–1914 are the most vital. Sadly we have been unable to present these in the original. (In fact we are only presenting an indication of the pictorial sources of Constructivism.) In these reliefs of Tatlin we can see in the destruction of the picture-frame, the abandonment of brush and colour, the desire to do away with pictorial illusion, a movement, as the artist himself described it, 'into real space and real materials'. From illusion to reality, from art into life. Although directly stemming from Picasso's Cubism, this artistic compulsion to break down pictorial language gained a quite different significance, as one can see in retrospect, in the world of pre-revolutionary Russia. One can see in it the foreshadowing of this urge to bring art into contact with everyday life which we find in the 'street art' of post-1917 already mentioned. It is the converging of this artistic and social urge which makes up Constructivism.

Architecture is the central field of Constructivist achievement, for in architecture one can most successfully create a way of life, a new order, touching every aspect of man's activity. Such and no less was the aim of the Constructivists. In the theatre of course one can create the illusion, or vision, of this new world, and for this reason the key productions represent Constructivism particularly effectively. This is perhaps even more the case with film where, through montage (as Eisenstein saw so clearly), the artist can manipulate and rearrange images of actual life. Other Constructivists were more modest and pragmatic in their attempts to transform everyday life – the former painters Popova, Rodchenko and Stepanova tried to become 'artist/engineers', turning their easel techniques to textiles, furniture and typographical design.

Much that we are showing in this exhibition will prove familiar to the visitor. For amazingly Constructivism is not only a chapter in the history of modern art, not only a story of dreams and plans and projects in far-off Russia of post-1917, it is the source of so many ideas which have actually shaped and vitally influenced our way of life. We hope with this exhibition to show the origin of these ideas and to establish their historic contribution in creating blueprints of modern design.

Art and Revolution in Soviet Russia
O A Shvidkovsky

The work of the Soviet architects and artists shown in this exhibition stems from a time of re-education and creative upsurge. Revolution was borne on waves of ideas, but some of these merely rolled the ship from side to side while others helped it forward. Today there is wide interest everywhere in Soviet art of the early post-Revolutionary period and the last decade has seen books and articles on this subject published in many languages. In the Soviet Union just now there is wide research into the history of Soviet theatre, painting, sculpture and applied arts, and collections of documents and illustrations relating to Soviet architecture are being published. Forgotten names are being rediscovered to give a fuller idea of the importance of the arts in the October Revolution and during the first decade of the Soviet Union. Art's energies, as Eisenstein has said, 'mobilise the experience of the past in the interests of the future'.

Literary instruction train 'October Revolution'

All major events in the arts reveal a context. For Soviet revolutionary art this context was the Socialist dream of progress. The spirit of the October Revolution was one of self-sacrifice in the name of change such as had been unknown in old Russia. The sphere of art was not merely altered: it grew a hundred times. The arts sought contact with the proletariat and freedom from the frames and curtains of the museums and the theatres. Artists engaged actively in the political struggle. Leaflets and speeches became the sharpest weapons of propaganda. Poets helped to give mass propaganda effective form. As Lunacharsky wrote in 1920: 'Revolution brings with it ideas of a wonderful depth and inner appeal. It inflames feelings of heroism and self-sacrifice. If revolution can give art a sword then art must give revolution its service.'

An outstanding role in mass propaganda was played by posters, which emerged in the very first days of the Revolution and at once became a basic necessity of everyday life. From the point of view of art their development was complex. At first they imitated book and magazine illustrations. Then a special technique of poster art was created, for which especial credit must go to Moor, Deni, Cheremnykh, and of course to Vladimir Mayakovsky. They aimed at simplicity and directness and achieved great popularity, and the enormous demand for them, and the large production, made them *the* art form dominating artistic life in those days. The ROSTA satirical posters drawn by Mayakovsky and his comrades spread around the Union. They were published in thirty-four towns, quickly reflecting topical events and commenting on them humorously. Other forms of mass propaganda included agit-trains and agit-ships, intended to link the centres of revolution, Moscow and Petrograd, with all Russia and with fronts active in the civil

Agit-ship

war. On these travelled officials and also poets and painters. The painters decorated the trains with images presenting topical messages in a simple and comprehensible manner. V I Lenin in 1918 promoted a plan for monumental propaganda in the streets of cities. Statues and plaques were set up to commemorate important workers for the Revolution, including artists, poets, musicians, and great philosophers and scientists of all the world. Few of these have remained since they often had to be made out of unsuitable but available materials such as plaster.

The first anniversary of the Revolution was the occasion for widespread mass propaganda work to which such artists as Altman, Kustodiev, Chagall, Kusnitsov, Lentulov, Tatlin, and the architect brothers Vesnin contributed. Altman had the interesting task of decorating the Palace Square in Petrograd. He placed symbolic shapes in bright colours around the column in the centre of the Square and decorated the streets converging on the Square as well as the facades forming it. Lunacharsky, People's Commissaire of Education, wrote that 'there has never been a festival, or workers' celebration, so beautiful in form'. There were paintings, banners, flags, garlands, triumphal arches; also satirical effigies of the enemies of the proletariat. The whole city was decorated with flags, surfaces were painted brightly, and the ships of the Baltic fleet steamed into the Neva. There was a great sense of holiday.

Similarly, the first post-Revolution years saw the development of the mass spectacle or mass theatre in which the struggle between the workers and the capitalists was graphically presented. The most famous instance is the re-enactment of the storming of the Winter Palace in Petrograd, witnessed by many who were involved in the original event and using the actual buildings and Square where it occurred. It is to be noted that this new form of art was created not from academic theory but through the pressures and needs occasioned by events.

Architecture holds a special place of honour in this time. Before the Revolution Russian architecture had a very chequered history. The nineteenth century saw academic historicism and also the influence of various Western styles notably the several versions of Art Nouveau, which were given a somewhat different colouring in Russia. The Revolution brought new social problems and new fields to conquer. Particularly it made demands on new processes of building and urgently pressed for new mass housing, new official buildings, new towns and development of the old. Lenin, at the 1919 Congress of the Communist Party, demanded the formulation of a policy of rebuilding suited to the new democratic society. This included better living conditions and also educational facilities, including easy access to artistic treasures. It stressed the need to liberate women from domestic routine by offering co-operative services.

Architectural progress was the result not of individual inventiveness but of the needs and spirit of the new Soviet society. In town planning the architect was faced with the double problem of improving conditions and easing congestion and of destroying the class distinctions which had shaped towns before. New town forms were put forward, notably by Ginsburg, Leonidov and Milutin, which are still of great value. Basing themselves on new systems of industrial building, planners tended to be either urbanists or disurbanists. Ladovsky produced the concept of an extendable garden city that has reappeared in recent times in the work of Doxiadis and others. Material limitations in these years alone inhibited the development of important new principles. Since there were few valid principles to be brought from the architecture of the past for application in the new society, there had to be a great deal of debate and discussion between the various experts. Some of the ideas that were tried out were Utopian and premature, as when architects attempted to force new social patterns on to the people and to make a complete break with patterns that had obtained. Yet in the projects of Ginsburg, the Vesnin brothers, Melnikov and others we see the beginnings of new collective principles, especially in housing, which reappear in the work of Le Corbusier and in that of various Czech and Polish architects.

An important new problem arose with the demand for workers' clubs and palaces, open libraries, Soviet governmental offices and so on. There could be no suitable prototypes for such buildings and architects had to find a form for them.

Ginsburg wrote in 1920 that 'if before the war and Revolution we tried new ideas, the last few years have shown that it is much easier for us to go forward when all are facing in the same direction'. On the way we found a new artistic language, corresponding to an era of technical and scientific revolution. Recent Soviet researchers (such as S O Khan-Mahomedov, A Strigalev and V Khazanova) have found a close link between the aesthetic search of those years and the new architectural forms, with architects at times coming close to the work of the modern painters. Different tendencies and groups came into being, notably the Rationalists led by Ladovsky and the Constructivists led by Alexander Vesnin. The Rationalists studied objective laws and psychology; the Constructivists stressed the technical effectiveness of their design and spoke of creating a new and beautiful life. Vesnin called on architects to 'enter into actual life, work in order to organise life, remember that the architect is the shaper of life; he is the appointed builder of socialism'. Ginsburg's book *Style and the Epoch* (1924) offered an analysis of this tendency. The journal *SA*, edited by Vesnin and Ginsburg, enjoyed a wide circulation. The projects and buildings of Melnikov, the Golosov brothers, Burov and others are of especial interest. We today place much importance on two completed projects which we consider Soviet classics: the Lenin Mausoleum and the Dneprpetrovsk hydro-electric station. The architect of the Mausoleum, Shusev, found a way of placing a small geometrical composition in the context of the Kremlin and the Church of St Basil, in Moscow, expressing important concepts and contributing permanently to official ceremonies. The creation of such a project sprang from a full realisation of the great powers called out by the Revolution.

In other areas of art and design the influence of the Revolution has been various and marked. New developments in theatrical design appear separate from the tradition of scene painting. The new theatrical design is synthetic. Thus in the set for Tairov's production of *Phèdre*, Alexander Vesnin was able to bring concentration to the action of the play by stressing a formality that reflects the intentions of Racine. Similarly, in his designs for the production of Claudel's *Annunciation*, Vesnin worked as a stage architect, organising space. For *The Man who was Thursday* he built a complex construction including three lifts, moving platforms, neon lights, telephones. Unfortunately these devices came to dominate the play. For Meyerhold's production of *The Magnanimous Cuckold* Popova designed a wood construction that could be set up anywhere. These and other developments required the closest physical and mental involvement of the audience and the productions – an aspect which has been much developed in recent years. The audience is rendered active, a participant in revolutionary events. Directors, actors and others pushed theatre in the same direction.

The development of the book in the Soviet Union was similar. The limitations set by shortages and an insufficient printing industry conflicted with the urgent need to bring literacy and literature to the people. At first artists could only decorate the new books, merely extending past traditions, but then they learned to draw effectively and simply in such a manner as to help the reader. There was a particularly brilliant development in the sphere of children's books, aided by the deeper understanding brought by child psychology. Of especial interest are the new methods associated with Rodchenko, Lissitzky and others of the *Lef* group. Rodchenko was the first to use photomontage on book covers and stressed the use of printing elements for book decoration. Externally the book could act as poster.

The Revolution had brought artists a unique opportunity and with it new inspiration, and they gave to it all they could according to their talents and individualities. Abstract art meant little to the people. Utopian dreams seemed too remote from practicalities – towns on springs, by Lavinsky; flying towns by Krutikhov; horizontal skyscrapers by Lissitzky. But were these merely useless? I do not think so. Such ideas belong to belief in progress and time has shown that such advanced ideas do not remain out of reach for ever. Inventors are necessary, and today we often return to ideas born in the immediate post-Revolution period as impulses for new research. After the cry 'Eureka!' comes the tiring process of study and calculation. In this exhibition we show something of the history linking the twenties with the present. The thirties and forties saw a popularisation of culture and the expression of a patriotism from which the world benefited in the fight against fascism. Within the changed stylistic idiom we find many of the new programmes of the twenties realised.

The poet Alexander Blok has said: 'In art there cannot be anything old.' Art does not stop but, on the contrary, continues to strengthen the progressive energy of the Soviet Revolution. The inspiration that motivated the architects, painters, sculptors and designers of the first post-Revolutionary years still operates in the Soviet Union.

Lenin speaking on 'Peace, Bread, Land'
Rodchenko photomontage

Lenin

From reading the 8 October issue of *Izvestia*, it appears that Comrade Lunacharsky said at the 'Proletkult' Congress exactly the opposite of what we had agreed on yesterday.

It is imperative to draw up without delay an outline for a resolution (of the congress of 'Proletkult'), to have it approved by the Central Committee and to pass a vote on it during this very session of the 'Proletkult'. On behalf of the Central Committee, we must submit it this very day to the Council of the People's Commissariat of Education and to the 'Proletkult' Congress because today is the last day of their session.

Outline for the Resolution

1 In the Soviet Republic of workers and peasants the whole education domain, both political education in general and more specifically art education, must be imbued with the spirit of class struggle experienced by the proletariat in order to realize the objectives of its dictatorship successfully, that is to overthrow the bourgeoisie, to abolish the classes, to suppress all exploitation of man by man.

2 This is why the proletariat, represented on the one hand by its avant-garde, the Communist Party, and on the other hand by all the different proletarian organisations in general, must play the most active and the most significant part in the whole domain of public education.

3 The experience of modern history and particularly that of more than fifty years of revolutionary struggle by the proletariat everywhere in the world, since the publication of the Communist Manifesto, proves beyond doubt that the Marxist conception of the world is the only correct expression of the interests, opinions and culture of the revolutionary proletariat.

4 Marxism has gained historic importance as ideology of the revolutionary proletariat because, far from refusing to acknowledge the greatest accomplishments of the bourgeois era, it has – on the contrary – assimilated and reconsidered all that had been valuable in human thought and culture for more than 2,000 years. It is only when performed on such a basis and with such an aim that work, prompted by experience of the proletariat dictatorship, last stage in its struggle against all exploitation, can be considered as the development of a truly proletarian culture.

Lenin

Outline for the Resolution:

1 No independent idea but Marxism.

2 No creation of a new proletarian culture but development of the best models, traditions, results of existing culture from the point of view of the marxist conception of the world, of the conditions of life and struggle of the proletariat at the time of its dictatorship.

3 Not outside the People's Commissariat of Education but as an integral part of it; because the Communist Party of Russia + the People's Commissariat of Public Education = the Σ of the Proletkult.

4 Close liaison and mutual subordination of the Prolekult and the People's Commissariat of Public Education.

5 Beware not . . . (here the manuscript is disrupted)

Written 9 October 1920

Translated (from the French) by Michèle Roberts

5 Keeping strictly to these principles, the Congress of the 'Proletkult' of Russia categorically dismisses, as being false in theory and harmful in practice, any attempt to create an independent culture, to confine itself to its specialised organisations, to limit the fields of action of the People's Commissariat of Education and of the 'Proletkult' or to set up 'the autonomy' of the 'Proletkult' within the instructions of the People's Commissariat of Education, etc. On the contrary the Congress makes it an absolute duty for all the organisations of 'Proletkult' to consider themselves entirely as auxiliary bodies to the network formed by the institutions of the People's Commissariat of Education and to accomplish their tasks under the general supervision of the Soviets (and more precisely of the People's Commissariat of Education) and of the Communist Party of Russia, as part of the tasks inherent to the dictatorship of the proletariat. . . .Comrade Lunacharsky says that his thought has been distorted. This resolution is therefore all the more necessary.

Written 8 October 1920
Published first 1926 in *Krasnaya Novy* III

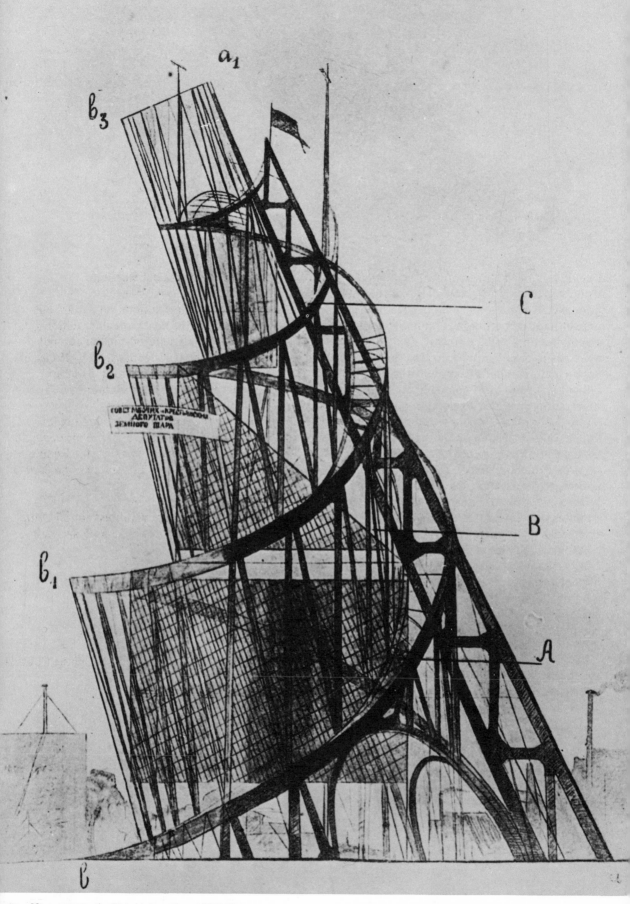

Monument to the Third International 1919–20

Notes on a
Lost Avant-Garde
Kenneth Frampton

Few projects in the history of contemporary architecture can compare in impact or influence to Vladimir Tatlin's 1920 design for a monument to the Third Internationale. In Russian avant-garde culture of this century, it occupies a position as a work of 'architecture' comparable to that held in painting by Malevich's 1913 designs for Kruchenik's Futurist play *Victory over the Sun*, out of which Suprematism immediately emerged. The importance of Tatlin's tower has now been generally acknowledged by architectural historians, yet even today few are willing to recognise the extent to which it crystallised a new consciousness which was to function as a continuous line of thought, sometimes covert, sometimes overt, in the development of European architecture between the two world wars. Central to this partially subterranean tradition was Tatlin's now well-known *Program of the Productivist Group*, also published in 1920, partly in response to the much more famous *Realist Manifesto* issued a few months previous by the brothers Gabo and Pevsner. The significance of this program lay in its conscious coinage of the term 'Constructivism'. The term, since then much misused, was given a rather exact formulation by those who invented it. The Productivist Group based the definition of Constructivism upon the subsequent definition of two additional compound terms, *'tektonika'* and *'faktura'*; the first referring to a complex of societal and industrial techniques, the second to the synthetic 'objectivity' of its unimpeded realisation.

'*Tektonika*' is derived from the structure of communism and the effective exploitation of industrial matter. Construction is organisation. It accepts the contents of the matter itself, already formulated. Construction is formulating activity taken to the extreme, allowing, however, for further 'tektonical' work. The matter deliberately chosen and effectively used, without however hindering the progress of construction or limiting the 'tektonika', is called '*faktura*' by the group.[1]

Constructivism was first and foremost seen as the act of construction conceived primarily as the organisation of a total technical capacity, specifically to be compounded out of communism and industrialisation. This manifestation of constructed or organised technique was thought of as the *fact*, or the *objective* inevitable actuality of Constructivism. The Constructivists regarded their raw material first of all as physical matter in general, consciously acknowledging its inherent nature and mode of production, and secondly as intellectual matter, that is, as light, plane, space, colour and volume. According to one contemporary critic, Alexei Gan, the Constructivists were to treat intellectual and solid materials in the same way. The Productionists (ie the Constructivists) were categorically against any gradual transition from ancient forms to the new scientific socialist mode of building. Their mood was apocalyptical. They were polemically extreme in their opposition to both art and religion. Their slogans extolled with almost Futurist fervour the virtues of industrial technology and socialist collectivity. They stood for an unmitigated utilitarianism, as may be seen from a later and more succinct definition of Constructivism that appeared in the Constructivist magazine *LEF* in 1923. This definition read as follows:

> Constructivism is the organisation of the given material on the principles of tectonics, structure and construction, the form becoming defined in the process of creation, by the utilitarian aim of the object.[2]

[1] For full text of programme see *Gabo*, Harvard University Press, 1957, p 153

[2] See *Futurism, Suprematism, Constructivism*, by Camilla Gray, article in *Soviet Survey*

Tatlin's Monument to the Third Internationale characterises this intention to consider *intellectual* and *physical* raw materials as equal elements in any given assembly or construction. However, one can hardly consider *its* form as having been creatively 'defined through the utilitarian aim of the object'.[3] In spite of the anti-art, anti-religion sloganeering of the Productivists, one can only consider the Tatlin Tower as primarily a symbolic structure. According to architect Berthold Lubetkin, a model of the tower was first exhibited under a ribbon which bore the slogan 'Engineers Create New Forms'. This ribbon was later borne through the streets by crowds of enthusiastic students. The millenialistic mechanico-idolatry of this project is clearly manifest in a contemporary description of it, which presumably paraphrases Tatlin's own words:

> The whole monument rests on two main axes which are closely connected. In the direction of these axes an upward movement is accomplished; this is crossed transversely at each of its points by the movement of the spirals... The chambers are arranged vertically above one another and surrounded by various harmonious structures. [Here the writer is referring to the glazed mobile elements contained within the superstructure.] By means of special machinery they are to be kept in perpetual motion but at different speeds. The lower chamber is *cubiform* and turns on its axis once a year; it is to be used for legislative purposes... The chamber above this is *pyramidal* in shape and makes one revolution a month; this is for the meetings of assemblies and executive bodies. Finally the third and the highest part of the building is in the shape of a *cylinder* and turns on its axis once a day. This part of the building will be used chiefly for administration and propaganda, that is, as a bureau of information, for newspapers, manifestos, etc. Telegraphs, radio-apparatus and projectors for cinematographic performances will be installed in this chamber...

In itself the use of spirals for monumental architecture means an enrichment of composition. Just as the triangle, as an image of general equilibrium, is the best expression of the Renaissance, so the spiral is the most effective symbol of the modern spirit of the age ... while the dynamic line of bourgeois society, aiming at possession of the land and the soil, was the horizontal, the spiral, which, rising from the earth, detaches itself from all animal, earthly and oppressing interests, forms the purest expression of humanity set free by the Revolution ... The monument unites the legislative with the executive and with the act of information; to each of these functions a position in space has been assigned corresponding to its nature. In this way and also by means of the chief building material used, the purity and clearness of initiative and its freedom from all material encumberance is symbolically indicated ...

Just as the product of the number of oscillations and the wavelength is the spatial measure of sound, so the proportion between glass and iron is the measure of material rhythm. By the union of these two fundamentally important materials, a compact and imposing simplicity and, at the same time, relation, is expressed, since these materials, for both of which fire is the creator of life, form the elements of modern art. By their union, rhythms must be created of mighty power, as though an ocean were being born. By the transformation of these forms into reality, dynamics will be embodied in unsurpassable magnificence, just as the pyramids once and for all expressed the principle of statics.[4]

[3] Despite the militant polemics Tatlin's utilitarianism was not of an ultra technocratic kind. As Kornely Zelinsky has observed there was much of the poet Khlebnikov in Tatlin's functionalism. This accounts for the 'dadaist' aura that pervades Tatlin's glider design of 1930; his famous Letatlin, its title compounded out of the verb 'to fly' and his own name. Zelinsky records Tatlin as remarking of his glider: 'I don't want people to take this thing purely as something utilitarian. Look at the bent wings. We believe them to be aesthetically perfect. Or don't you think "Letatlin" gives an impression of esthetic perfection? Like a hovering sea gull: Don't you think?' see *Vladimir Tatlin* by Troels Andersen, Moderna Museet, Stockholm, 1968, p 78

[4] *The Mind and Face of Boshevism*, by René Fülöp-Miller, Harper Torchbook, 1965, pp 101, 102

This passage with its valuation of iron and glass is rather typical of that peculiar mixture of millennialistic symbolism and utilitarian dialectic which abounded in the rhetoric of the Russian avant-garde during the immediate post-Revolutionary period. Sentences such as 'Rhythms must be created as of a mighty power, as though an ocean were being born' are obviously indebted to Futurism while the writer's reference to the pyramids recalls Eiffel's appeal to Egyptian monumentality, while defending the design of his tower in 1885. Tatlin no doubt saw his own monumental project not only as a homage to Eiffel, but also as an almost cabalistic celebration of the Revolution with its use of the three platonic solids and the logarithmic spiral, etc. This spiral form, symbolising the transcendental dynamism of the Revolution, was to be repeated as a constant motive in Soviet avant-garde work throughout the next decade.

The symbolic use of an ascending spiral has obvious antique and archaic precedents in the commemorative column and the apotropaic labyrinth, but its use in the modern area, that is since 1750, seems always to have been indicative of a transcendental symbolism of 'social revolutionary' content. A demonstration of this is to be found in Carola Giedion-Welcker's study of contemporary sculpture wherein Tatlin's tower is compared with Hermann Obrist's monument of 1902 and with Rodin's project for a monument to labour of 1897. To this remarkable series one might venture to add Etienne Boullée's late eighteenth-century design for a truncated cone-shaped tower, which like the Obrist monument features a procession of figures with linked hands spiralling up towards its summit.

Tatlin's Tower was the initial symbolic crystallisation of a Constructivist aesthetic which on subsequent occasions would occur as the direct expression of a utilitarian rationale. The use of industrial materials, the expression of literal movement, the emphasis on dynamic form, the exhibition of both structure and function, combined with the direct incorporation of information and propaganda to reflect the ethos of a secular era, dedicated to the rationalisation of human life through organised industrialisation.

Vesnin brothers
Project for Pravda building 1923–4

Typical of the direct development of this aesthetic in the service of an actual building programme was the Vesnin brothers' 1923 project for the *Pravda* newspaper building, of which the Russian avant-garde graphist and architect El Lissitzky wrote in 1929 as follows:

> All the accessories of the city street such as signs, advertisements, loudspeakers, etc, are integrated into this building. They are treated as equal elements in the design and assembled into an entity. This is the aesthetic of Constructivism.[5]

In this small building, about 19 by 19 feet in plan, the Vesnin brothers projected a clear expression of a skeleton frame. Within its glazed skin twin elevators would have shuttled back and forth to serve each of its six floors. The whole building was clearly meant to be understood as an industrial product in which the mobile elements such as doors, windows, elevators, etc, were of the same component calibre as the ancillary equipment – the red flag, the searchlight, the numerical clock, the loudspeaker and the rotating billboard.

This project seen in retrospect holds its own as a canonical work with other avant-garde European projects of comparable date, such as Le Corbusier's Ozenfant studio, Rietveld's Schroeder house or Mies van der Rohe's glass skyscraper project, all of the years 1922–23. The essentially 'synthetic' nature of Constructivism is made explicit by this comparison; the *Pravda* project is the only work consciously designed to assimilate into its form an extensive range of non-architectural media.

The direct structural articulation of the *Pravda* building, the transparency of its facade, the expressive mobility of its components and the empirical determination of its arrangement are each in turn characteristic of the Constructivist aesthetic as it was to evolve during the early twenties. The underlying utilitarian rationale led frequently to mechanistic fantasia which often made such an idealisation of the appearance of utility as to involve a sacrifice in actual convenience. The avant-garde could well afford in the early years of Soviet *Sturm und Drang* to be indifferent to issues such as commodity or economy. Far more important for many designers, in the heat of the unrealisable moment, was a dynamic image equal to the iconoclastic appeal of everyday polemics. In such a climate the initial principles of the Productivist programme were often misinterpreted or deliberately abandoned. Only artists of high calibre and conviction such as Tatlin and Rodchenko were able to work throughout the twenties, as industrial designers, and to produce thereby a range of utilitarian equipment such as stoves, collapsible furniture, working overalls, ceramics, utensils, etc, which were specifically conceived for the actual needs of a semi-nomadic proletariat. Immediately after the Russian Revolution both Tatlin and Rodchenko were involved in teaching in the Moscow Vchutemas. Late in the nineteen twenties Tatlin went to teach and work in Petrograd. At the same time Rodchenko went to Inhuk where he organised the 'artist/engineer' Constructivist group with which El Lissitzky was to be briefly associated. After this date all sorts of esthetic factions began to emerge in association with varying shades of political and technical opinion.

The architect Ladovsky initiated a typical splinter group during this period. His atelier propagated a school in which formal systems were to be generated partly out of utility and partly out of the principles of Gestalt psychology. His 1924 design for a suspended restaurant, in which a utilitarian expression of structure and movement is combined with a rhythmic progression of glazed prismatic volumes, is a polemical *tour de force* in this manner – although hardly a rational solution to the problem of a restaurant. Although the Ladovsky group advocated an 'objective' architecture, its end product was permeated by an ideal vocabulary of symbolic forms which were deemed to be expressive of typical psychic states such as 'tranquility', 'integrity', etc. It amounted, as Berthold Lubetkin has pointed out, to a universalism of a Larousse type which was in the last analysis highly subjective.[6]

---

[5] *Russland: Die Rekonstruktion der Architektur in der Sowjet-union*, by El Lissitzky, Vienna 1930, p 13

[6] See *The Builders* by Berthold Lubetkin, *Architectural Review* May 1932

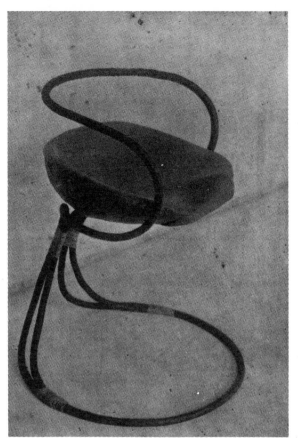

Tatlin
Bent-tube chair with moulded seat c 1927

Rodchenko in the workers' costume he designed 1920

El Lissitzky, architect, painter, photographer, propagandist, typographer and theoretician, was the synthetic artist *par excellence* of a cultural movement which was by definition synthetic. His 'Proun' art work, its very name being a contraction of *Pro* and *Unovis* (ie For the New Art),[7] was in his own words seen as an *Umsteigestation* or 'interchange station' from painting to architecture. Typical of such work is his famous Lenin Tribune project of 1920, which implied an architecture as synthetic in respect of the whole visual environment as the Vesnin brothers' *Pravda* building of 1923.

A more revealing three-dimensional work was Lissitzky's *Prounen-Raum* built for the Grosse Berliner Kunstaustellung of 1923, in which he attempted to destroy, through the agency of a structured wall relief, the constraining box-like quality of the available space and to create out of it a new 'Suprematist-Elementarist' entity.

Two years later in his essay *K und Pangeometrie* he was to write of such space: 'We see that Suprematism has swept away from the plane the illusions of two-dimensional planimetric space, the illusions of three-dimensional perspective space and has created the ultimate illusion of *irrational* space, with infinite extensibility into the background and foreground.'[8] For Lissitzky the illusion of infinite space implied and indeed demanded actual flexibility in use. Thus he was to write of his *Prounen-Raum*: 'The equilibrium which I seek to attain in the room must be elementary and capable of change, so that it cannot be disturbed by a telephone or a piece of standard office furniture. The room is there for the human being – not the human being for the room.'[9] With such a 'humanist' synthesis Lissitzky sought to bridge the polemical gap that divided the utilitarianism of Tatlin from the 'non-objective' world of Malevich.

[7] Malevich renamed the Vitebsk school UNOVIS; these initials standing for 'College of the New Art', see *The Great Experiment: Russian Art 1863–1922* by Camilla Gray, London 1962, p 227

[8] Lissitzky-Küppers. *El Lissitzky*, Thames & Hudson London 1968, p 350, translated by Helene Aldwinckle

[9] Lissitzky-Küppers, op cit p 361

Lissitzky envisaged a world in which differences between various metiers were to be minimised to bring about the realm of the 'artist/engineer'. His versatile talent was able to assemble a spectrum of heterogeneous objects which, irrespective of their different media, were rendered as complementary parts of a single socialist universe. Paradoxically his later non-metaphorical architectural projects appear to be subject to a greater differentiation.

His 1925 *Wolkenbügel* project, designed in association with Mart Stam, is a building entirely detached from the earth, which may account for its depiction as an object free from either kinetic or graphic elements. This is an avant-garde project even by today's standards where the past decade has seen proposals for similar structures by Kenzo Tange and Yona Friedman. Located at intersections along a concentric Moscow Boulevard, the *Wolkenbügel*

were essentially *propylaea*, *elevated* high above the main thoroughfares leading to the city centre and the Kremlin. As such they appear to have been comparable to Ledoux's Parisian *barrières*, while remaining the very antithesis of such monumentality. It is evident that Lissitzky recognised the radical nature of such a proposal, for he wrote of it in his book *Russland* of 1929, as follows: 'In comparison with the American skyscraper, the innovation here resides in the fact that the "utilised" space which is horizontal, is clearly separated from the services or support space which is vertical', and again, 'Externally we are presented with an entity in space which from all six directions is an elementarist diversity.'[10]

[10] El Lissitzky, op cit p 30

Lissitzky
Wolkenbügel in Nikitsky Square, Moscow 1925 (montage)

The 'Suprematist-Elementarist' vision of dematerialised universe is embodied in Lissitzky's concepts of imaginary space, wherein space becomes apparent solely by virtue of movement. This illusionistic creation of space through movement of either object or spectator seems to have implied for Lissitzky a corresponding dematerialisation of form. From this stems Lissitzky's preoccupation with the suspension of structures clear of the earth of which he wrote in *Russland*: 'Our idea for the future is to minimise the foundations that link to the earth. We have developed this idea already in a series of projects.'[11] This was a reference not only to his *Wolkenbügel* project, but more specifically to Ivan Leonidov's 1927 project for the Lenin Institute to be erected outside Moscow. With this competition entry for an institute of advanced study, Leonidov emerged into prominence from his obscure background as a painter and from his Vchutemas education and his subsequent work in the Vesnin atelier. His entire contribution was to be made within the next three years.

Leonidov was the last significant figure to emerge out of the milieu of the Russian architectural avant-garde prior to the advent of Stalinism. His output is to be distinguished from more 'utilitarian-objective' or, on occasion, more 'formalistic' work of his immediate colleagues by virtue of its simplicity, elegance, delicacy and aura of ineffability. Although it was not subject to a rigorous utilitarianism, it postulated an architecture that was free from rhetoric. This, combined with its intangible air of other-worldliness, now tends to project it more into our own foreseeable future than any other pioneer work of the same era. Leonidov shares with Lissitzky the honour of having anticipated the work of much of our own architectural avant-garde. Various elements in his work suggest in turn Wachsman, Le Ricolais, Buckminster Fuller, Friedman, Otto, Price and even Malcolmson.

Leonidov's Lenin Institute consisted of a library tower (15,000 books) and an elevated spherical auditorium (40,000 persons!), plus a series of horizontal study buildings. The whole complex was designed for connection to the city centre by an aerial railway. In 1927 its originality did not pass unrecognised. For Lissitzky it was 'a physically dynamic architecture of floating volumes', while for the

architect Ginsburg, writing in 1927, its urban implications were clear. Ginsburg wrote, 'It dismisses traditional solutions and leads towards a new conception of urban space in which such a building would be able to find its place.'[12]

Leonidov
Design for the Lenin Institute 1927

Leonidov's conception of urban space was like that of Lissitzky's, an 'open city' or 'ville verte' which superseded in its formulation the then current rival Soviet theories of 'urbanism' and 'disurbanism'. Like Lissitzky, he was acutely aware that the urban structure of an unprecedented socialist mass society would automatically demand new 'social condensers' for its effective organisation. His 1927 Lenin Institute and his 1930 Cultural Palace/Park are both attempts at formulating such 'condensers'.

[11] *Ville et Revolution*, by Anatole Kopp, Paris, 1967, p 203

[12] The struggle between the 'urbanists' and the 'deurbanists' turned on the issue of the way in which a socialist population should be redistributed. The former favoured their being housed in open country in high rise superblocks or *unités*, close to the units of production; the latter recommended their dispersal in two storey individual homes.

Simple prismatic glazed forms, suspension techniques and metallic geodesic construction are common elements in both projects. In each case the larger structures enclose unobstructed micro-environments, such as auditoriums, winter gardens, etc. These envelopes are climate-controlled and technically homogenous. Elevational manipulation is always reduced to the minimum. There is no attempt to borrow public 'urban space use' conceptions from the past, such as the agora, etc. The approach is hedonistic, while remaining at the same time 'objective'. The dirigible and its mooring mast are to be seen as pertaining to the same technical system as the earthbound structures. No plastic event occurs for the sake of enlivening the surfaces.

In 1930 Leonidov played a leading role in the OSA group's design for the new town of Magnitogorsk. This plan was a development of Milutin's linear city concept, the town being designed as a continuous road settlement linking inland agriculture to a lakeside steel works. Leonidov's contribution is evident in the design of the housing sector and the layout of the cultural park on either side of the arterial road. The housing was arranged in unit clusters of eight 'communes' each commune comprising sixteen individual rooms arranged on two floors around a cruciform common area, divided into winter garden, lounge, gymnasia and playcourts. Such a proposal offered a much more human form of socialist settlement than the barrack-like high-rise communes or the super blocks then being generally postulated by Leonidov's contemporaries.

Both the commune block developed by the 'urbanists' and the linear system of low density urban settlement projected by the OSA group of 'deurbanists', were to exert a lasting influence on the work of Le Corbusier. The one was to be developed into his *Ville Radieuse* section of 1933; the famous duplex apartment unit that was to be finally realised in his *Unité d'Habitation, Marseille*. The other was to be reformulated by him as the linear industrial city of his comprehensive regional planning thesis, as published in his book *Les Trois Etablissements Humains* of 1945.

The OSA group, started by Moses Ginsburg and the Vesnin brothers, was to emerge out of the early NEP period to become the ideological forum of Soviet architecture after 1926. The organ of this group, *Sovremennaya Arkhitektura* or *SA* became the one important Soviet architectural journal, through which ideas and issues could constantly be exchanged and debated, both internally and with the West. It continued to perform this function until its forcible closure in 1931. OSA, an association which embraced artists and engineers, as well as architects, was to dedicate itself to defining the nature of the socialist architect's task. These it was finally to formulate in the first and last OSA conference of 1928. This conference came out against abstract formal research or play, where this was divorced from a rigorous concern for programme and social function, as in the works of ASNOVA, (ie Lissitzky, Ladovsky, Melnikov, etc). It also opposed the incipient party line attempt to revive the old 'nationalist' styles of bourgeois culture. The ideological lines were most distinctly drawn by Ginsburg when he declared that: ... 'the elementary approach typical of most architects almost mechanically leads to their treating workers housing in the same way as they would bourgeois apartments. Strictly speaking the only difference is in the size of the rooms ... The constructivists however approach the same problem with maximum considerations for those shifts and changes in our way of life that are preparing the way for a completely new type of housing ... that is to say that for us the goal is not the execution of a commission as such, but collaboration with the proletariat in its task of building a new life, a new way of living.[13]

[13] Kopp op cit pp 99, 100

An earlier version of this article was previously
published in *Art News Annual* xxxiv, 1968.

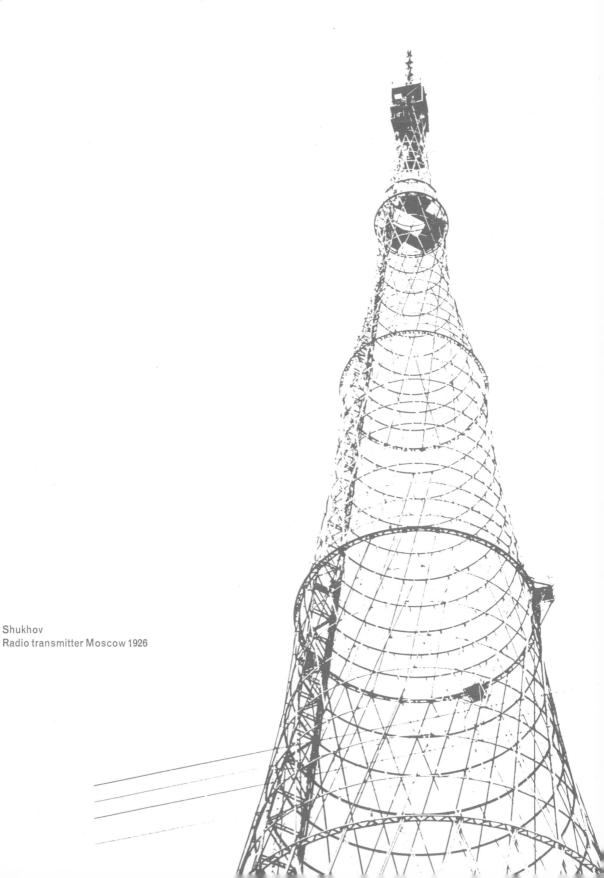

Shukhov
Radio transmitter Moscow 1926

Soviet Architecture and Town Planning of the Twenties
S O Khan-Mahomedov

The first period of Soviet architecture occupies a special place in the history of world architecture. During that time our architecture developed into the only Socialist architecture in the world.

The radical reforms of those days compelled our architects to concentrate on fundamental problems. Many who put forward new ideas in the twenties were looking so far ahead that their exploratory projects and proposals have only recently received recognition and practical realisation.

During the very first years after the Revolution, creative architecture found itself living under the difficult conditions created by civil war and economic chaos. Also, Tsarist Russia had left an awkward heritage in the realm of architecture. The relative conservatism of the most influential trends of pre-Revolutionary Russian architecture (varying shades of eclecticism and stylisation) impeded the search for a new creative trend.

A discernible new trend emerged out of the early struggle. Its followers had concentrated on searching for new types of buildings and on finding a new artistic idiom. This search was directly influenced by new trends in fine art and literature that appeared in Russia even before the first World War in opposition to official academic art. Painters, sculptors and poets played an active part in setting up revolutionary festivities, marches, meetings and demonstrations.

The great changes the country went through after the October Revolution could naturally not find immediate reflection in architecture. Life altered visibly but the towns remained as they were. This contradiction, sharply felt at that time, between the new content of life and the old architecture, brought energy into artistic design and monumental art. Placards, slogans, posters, propaganda leaflets covered the walls of houses. Art literally bespattered the streets, striving to reconcile the outward appearance of the towns with the lives lived in them. In 1918 Lenin put forward his famous plan for monumental propaganda, in which he foresaw the role of propaganda art and the erection of memorials to revolutionaries and to cultural workers. 'The streets are our brushes. The squares our palettes' proclaimed Mayakovsky. He and many others were involved in designing festivals, propaganda trains, etc, among them being N Altman, A Rodchenko, V Tatlin, K Malevich, N Gabo, V Stepanova, L Popova, L Lissitsky, A Gan, D Sternberg, K Petrov-Vodkin, M Dobuzhinsky, A Lentoluv, M Chagall and I Novinsky.

Propaganda art was closely linked to architecture. It included smaller architectural projects such as speakers' platforms (eg the Lenin rostrum by Lissitzky, 1920), shop windows and kiosks, and could not help but be an influence on architecture itself, the more so because many architects took an active part in working on the design and building of monuments. For example, the Vesnins designed the Red Square for the post-Revolutionary May-day parades, L Rudnev built the memorial 'To those who sacrificed themselves for the Revolution' in Petrograd with texts by A Lunacharsky, and an obelisk to the Soviet Constitution was raised in Moscow to D Osipov's design.

Street decoration, probably 1921. Exhortation to increase timber production. Linking town and country

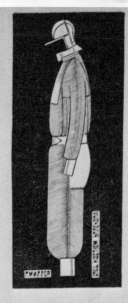

нашего века конструктивизму не удалось с достаточной отчетливостью осуществить свои задачи и привлечь на свою сторону квалифицированные рабочие силы той или иной специальности, то современная передовая архитектура у нас и в Германии уже установила теснейшую связь с конструктивизмом. В РСФСР конструктивизм принят полиграфическим производством. Две такие огромные материальные области художественного труда, как архитектурное строительство и фабрика печатной вещи, с нами.

Это, несомненно, факты огромного значения и в этом залог новых побед конструктивизма в будущем.

АЛЕКСЕЙ ГАН

Арматура улицы. Складной станок с лотком для уличной торговли папиросами или бумагой и писчебумажными принадлежностями. Улица так же как и квартира требует рабочей обстановки. Конструктивизм и сюда должен направить свое внимание и наблюдать за бытом улицы. Станок сделал в 1922 году Алексей Ган, дар Моссельпрома.

ФАКТЫ ЗА НАС

Работы конструктивистов свидетельствуют о том, что конструктивизм не только на словах разрешал проблему рационализации художественного труда, но и на деле уже осуществляет новые его виды, участвуя в строительстве материальной культуры дня.

Наша техническая отсталость не дает конструктивистам возможности развернуть работу во всю ширь и поставить дело создания и сооружения вещи так, чтобы теперь же, идя навстречу новой общественной потребности целесообразного овеществления повседневного быта—ее реально удовлетворять. Этого еще нет. Но так крепки и здоровы основы конструктивизма, так силен его художественный материализм, что и в этих тяжелых условиях он все же заговорил практическим языком дела.

А ведь всего каких-нибудь пять-шесть лет назад никому и в голову не приходило подумать, что этот практический язык найдется и что его создадут те самые люди, которые с таким темпераментом и с такой настойчивостью восстали тогда против старых видов искусства во имя новых видов художественного труда.

Взглянув на художественную действительность наших дней, именно теперь, как-то особенно резко бросается в глаза разделение двух, противопоставленных друг другу, культур.

С одной стороны, художественная культура прошлого, традиционное искусство в его старых видах: станковой живописи, графики, скульптуре, пластике, театре и подражающей прошлому архитектуре; с другой—новые виды художественного труда, базирующиеся на науке, технике, механике и оптике,—это полиграфия, фотография, кинематография, вещь, проз- и спец-одежда, физкультура, массовое действо и современная архитектура, как организация и сооружение новых материальных организмов прогрессивного общества.

Все это говорит за то, что пришло время действительно считаться с фактами.

Если еще в целом ряде областей материальных ценностей художественной культуры

СТОЛ предназначен для письменной работы, черчения и обеда. В нижнюю часть стола могут убираться 4 складные стула, а также из нижней части (подставки) выдвигаются с обеих сторон конверты для журналов, газет и бумаг. Крышка одной половины стола поднимается вместе с боковыми сторонами и, занимая вертикальное положение, открывает стол для обеда, на котором имеется передвижная в прорезах дорожка (скатерть).

В поднятой вертикальной доске имеются откидные полки, а ниже кольца и ремни для обеденного и чайного сервиза. Опускаясь, верхняя крышка накрывает обеденный стол, не касаясь посуды, и ее обратная сторона может быть использована для работы. Вторая часть стола приподнимается около крайнего ребра и может дать любой наклон для черчения. Кроме того, стол имеет ряд ящиков, предназначенных для хранения чертежей, рабочих материалов и принадлежностей. Ножки стола поставлены на шарики, и весь стол может быть легко передвинут и вовсе разобран. Проект конструктивиста Морозова. Москва. Вхутемас. Металлический факультет. 1926 год.

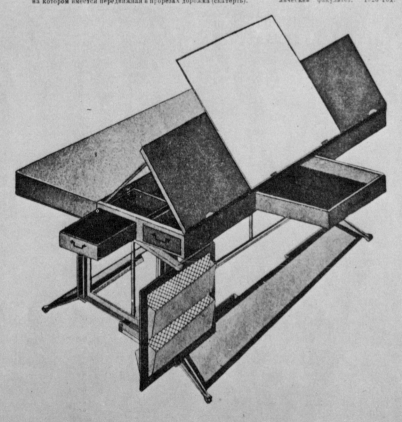

The most famous piece of propaganda art was the Memorial to the Third International designed by V Tatlin in 1919. It represents a framework constructed on a spiral, containing three buildings, placed one on top of the other – conference halls, an administrative block and an information centre. This exciting new project was praised by architectural communities everywhere. The romantic symbolism of its exterior helped architects to surmount the psychological barrier which prevented them from finding a new architecture, fusing new forms with contemporary meaning. Tatlin's tower had no less a significance in his time than did Eiffel's at the end of the nineteenth century.

The part played by artists in this search for new forms is naturally reflected in projects containing features of romantic symbolism, distinguished by an emphasis on novelty. Their significance lay in their formal and aesthetic experiments in the grouping of simple geometric patterns (Malevich), the combining of different materials (Tatlin), the use of colour (Lissitsky) and so on. This involvement produced the opposite effect also, in that many artists, working closely with architects over this period, became the first Soviet industrial designers (Tatlin, Rodchenko, Gan, Stepanova, the brothers V and G Stenberg, and others).

A decree of the Soviet of People's Commissars, signed by Lenin late in 1920, authorised the setting up of the Vkhutemas (Higher artistic and technical school), where architectural, industrial and artistic facilities were combined in one building. Here great architectural pioneers taught, people like N Ladovsky, K Melnikov, A and L Vesnin, I and P Golosov, M Ginsburg, V Krinsky. Within the walls of the Vkhutemas heated arguments were commonplace, new ideas were born and experiments were made. The work of the students of Vkhutemas was widely published not only in the Soviet Union, but also in architectural publications abroad.

The basic principles which defined the development of Soviet architecture of the twenties took shape under the influence of the radical social reforms. However, creatively and practically speaking, this trend was not integral. Within it, at the beginning of the twenties, were two distinct movements – the rationalists and the constructivists.

The leader of the rationalists was N Ladovsky. Around him in the early stages was a group of painters, sculptors and architects (Zhivskulptarch, 1919) and, later in 1920, a group studying objective analysis and a working group of architects (in the Institute of Art and Culture). All the time, he was gathering men with creative talent who had the same ideas as he into a group which in 1923 became ASNOVA (Association of New Architects). The rationalists spent a great deal of time on the search for a new art form, making full use of the very latest building materials and constructions and attaching great importance to objective considerations in compositional structure.

Ladovsky was one of the first architects of the twentieth century to question seriously the perceptual basis of architectural and artistic forms. He considered it necessary to analyse the psycho-physiological regularities of architectural shapes, spaces and colours. In discussing rational aesthetics and rational architecture ('ratio-architecture'), Ladovsky meant above all to discriminate objective rules. He established in Vkhutemas a laboratory for scientific research with a view to supporting intuition with the facts of psycho-physiological perception. He urged people to look for fundamentally new architectural solutions. He realised that creative fantasy played a large part in the growth of such a solution, and knew that one of the most important problems facing the architectural school was the development of a capacity for three-dimensional invention.

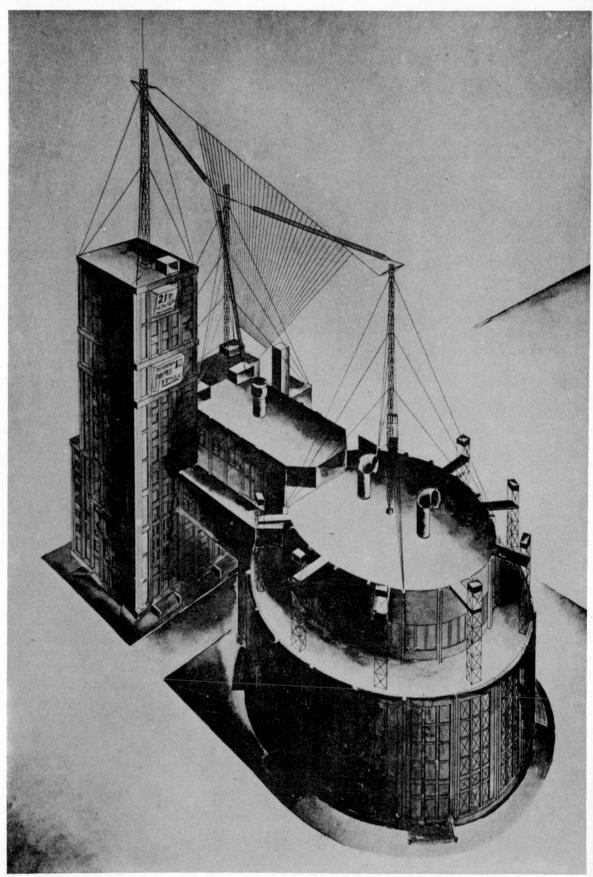

Vesnin brothers
Palace of Labour

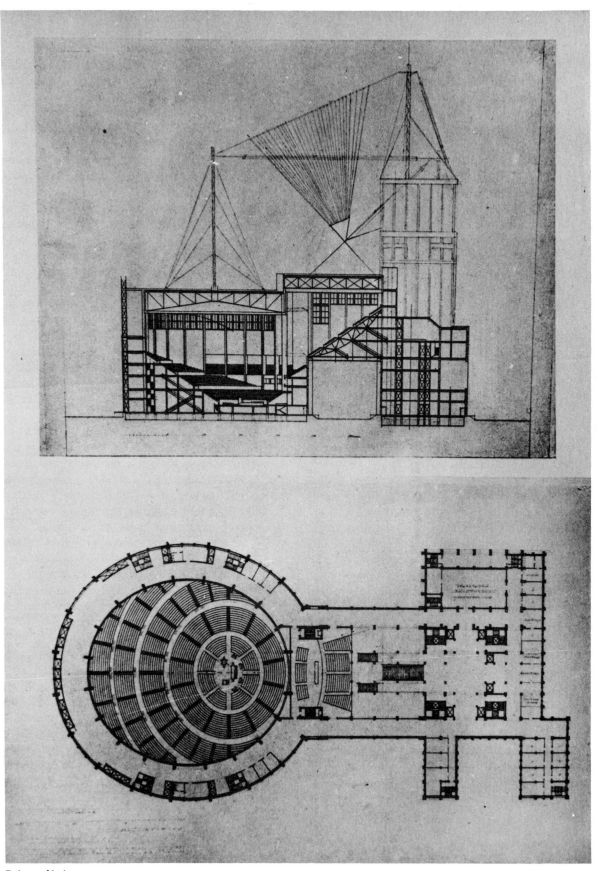

Palace of Labour

His psycho-analytical method of teaching won the Vkhutemas an honorary diploma at the Paris Decorative Arts exhibition in 1925.

This method aimed at developing flexibility. Ladovsky suggested to his students that they should undertake individual study of the laws of art and composition, using the concepts of psycho-physiology. They studied the basic aspects of spatial form: surface, volume and interior space and also elements of composition in architecture, such as proportion, rhythm, colour, dynamics, etc. The syllabus foresaw not only the complexities of spatial form and its surroundings but also a gradual fusion of compositional and constructive demands.

Emphasising the importance, in artistic matters, of calculating the form of the objective regularities of psycho-physiological perception, the rationalists turned their attention to the search for new forms for new types of residential and social buildings reflecting social change.

The second movement, constructivism, finally came into being a few years later than rationalism. The theoretical credo of constructivism reflected the new conditions for the development of architecture when, after the end of the civil war, the need for practical building became obvious. The constructivists emphasized the importance of functional and constructive factors and went into action on two fronts: against restoration and against 'the formalism of the left' in which category they placed some of the supporters of ASNOVA.

Constructivism appeared at the beginning of 1923 in a project by the Vesnins for the Palace of Labour in Moscow. An important competition held for the Palace of Labour showed which path Soviet architecture was likely to follow. It called for designs for a grandiose public building complex in the centre of Moscow (where the Moscow Hotel was later built).

This would contain a House of Councils, a Palace of Congress, a theatre, a House of Culture, town committee rooms, a museum, a dining room, etc. The main hall had to seat 8,000 and the smaller hall, 2,500 people. Most entrants (about 50 in all) designed the Palace of Labour in a traditional monumental style. The innovatory plan of the brothers Vesnin stood out. Its contemporary appearance, drawn to an exact and rational plan and its bold use of the latest structural materials far outshone its rivals.

Many architects saw in the Vesnin project an answer to their search. It was the first time that the social content of a new type of public building had organically led, through functional and technical factors, to a new architectural form. The Vesnins were recognised as leaders of the constructivist movement, but they shared the theoretical platform with Ginsburg. In *Style and the Epoch* (1924) Ginsburg, arguing with the eclectics as much as the rationalists, emphasised and substantiated the logic of the new architectural form.

In 1925 the constructivists set up their own organisation, OSA (Union of Contemporary Architects), the nucleus of which had been formed as early as 1922–24 in the architectural group of LEF (A Vesnin and others), a group of Ginsburg's followers in Moscow and, later, in a group of architects led by A Nikolsky in Leningrad. Despite the difference of opinion on theoretical and creative matters between the rationalists (ASNOVA) and the constructivists (OSA), both movements contributed greatly to the development of the Soviet architecture of the twenties and successfully complemented each other.

This tendency did not, however, win the day until 1925. It was helped by the competitions of 1924 and 1925 for the design of such buildings as the Moscow branch of the newspaper *Pravda* involving Melnikov, the Vesnins and others. Two of the resulting projects stand out through their artistic merit and the influence they had on contemporary architecture.

Vkhutemas students
Market project

The first is the Vesnin's plan for *Pravda*. A combination of factors gave this building its coherent and at the same time avant-garde character – the balanced composition, the delicately contrived proportion of the elevation and the harmony of reinforced concrete, framing windows of metal and glass.

The second project is the Soviet Pavilion in Paris. This was designed in 1925 by Melnikov, a member of ASNOVA, one of the most influential architects of the twenties. It was the first time that a Soviet architect had moved into the world arena and triumphantly at that. The Soviet pavilion stood out among the eclectic, traditional efforts of almost all other countries because of its contemporary look. The simple geometric forms, the bold use of colour, the framework of wood and glass, the original use of an outside staircase (to break the parallelogram of the two-storey building with a diagonal line) all made a great impression on the architects of many countries.

Over the years 1926–30 the theoretical and professional basis for Soviet architecture was discussed in the magazine *Contemporary Architecture* (*SA*). The main argument centred on functionalist attitudes. The so-called functionalist method became better known when Ginsburg expounded its principles in a series of theoretical articles. In his leading article for the first edition of *SA* Ginsburg wrote: 'The attitude of the contemporary architect to the formulation of new ideas is closely linked to our everyday lives.' The constructivists considered that the function of a building should be paramount. The functionalist attitude affected the entire creative programme of the time. Architects were compelled to work on new types of building, fighting against eclecticism, injecting new scientific and technical know-how into architecture so as to reveal its aesthetic potential, and fighting for the industrialisation and typification of construction and the breaking down of buildings into a series of standardised elements which could be manufactured at a factory. Advocating scientific planning, the constructivists simplified the complex relationship of the functional significance of a building with its spatial composition. They also overstated the meaning of purely rational factors in architectural creativity so that their introduction of the latest technical achievements into building seemed inevitable.

In subsequent years Soviet architecture faced the need to overcome one-sided theories in the attitudes and practical work of the rationalists and constructivists. During the second half of the twenties when the functional method of the constructivists and the formal-aesthetic search of the rationalists had already enjoyed considerable success an issue arose which fused these achievements.

Leonidov contributed greatly to solving this, a very gifted artist as well as an inventor and thinker. His diploma-winning project for the Institute of Library Science (commonly known as the Lenin Institute) was shown in 1927 at the first exhibition of contemporary architecture in Moscow and made an enormous impression on those who saw it. The project was highly praised by A Vesnin, who saw in it the birth of a new architecture, and Ginsburg wrote: 'A brilliantly executed series of fine graphic drawings and a model, exactly illustrating its

bold architectural and spatial concept, make us prize this work as a categorical breakthrough from that system of devices, schemes and elements, which inevitably has become usual and widespread, at best with unity of method as a result, at worst with threats of cliches of style.'

The proposal was for a vast complex to be built on the Lenin Hills, consisting of a library, institutes for scientific research, auditoria, etc. The decision to have such a large auditorium was unusual and considered to be a step forward. Leonidov designed it in the form of a vast sphere, held above the ground by open-work metal supports. The top half of the sphere was glazed, an amphitheatre occupied the lower half. Beside the main auditorium stood the vertical parallelepiped of the library.

Although Leonidov did not succeed in getting any of his large-scale projects built, his influence was felt all over the world. In 1928–30 he designed a great many projects – brilliant in their depth of thought and professionalism, and also in their graphic layout. Among others there were the Tsentrosoyuz (1928), the House of Industry (1929–30) and a Palace of Culture (1930) for Moscow, and a Socialist settlement for the Magnitogorsk group of enterprises. New issues were raised by these projects – such as the place of a cultural and social complex in the building of a town of the future, the spatial organisation of contemporary towns, links between urban areas and the countryside. Architects were greatly influenced by Leonidov's attitude to composition. He was one of the first to show the tendency to formal simplicity in modern architecture. This received recognition only in the 1940s. He showed that simple geometric volumes, devoid of decoration, possess more significance than intentionally complicated designs. During the 1920s, when many others were hoping to find a modern content in complex architectural grouping, his insistence on the most laconic design was innovatory to say the least.

Soviet architecture of the twenties was characterised by intense activity kept public and under discussion by the sequence of open competitions. These focused attention on the main problems facing architects and society, and in this way a synthesis of the rationalist and constructivist trends came about in the later twenties.

Interior of Type F-1 flat

There was a severe lack of housing for the working class in Tsarist Russia. Families huddled together in basements, wooden huts, hovels, barns and in doss-houses where they were provided with bunks or (for a family) the corner of a room.

From the earliest days of the October Revolution, the party concentrated on the need to improve the workers' living conditions. A massive resettling began, with workers being moved into houses confiscated from the bourgeoisie. In Moscow alone, from 1918 to 1924, 500,000 people were rehoused in this way. The Party planners had also quickly begun to introduce a building scheme. Most effort went into the search for a new type of house and for a new principle for the design of housing complexes – all of which links with the social problems associated with the reforming of the worker's way of life and with improving women's lot.

V I Lenin wrote in 1919: 'Woman continues to remain a *household slave*, despite all liberating laws, for she is humiliated and weighed down, suffocated and dazed by the *petty household chores*, chaining her to the kitchen and the nursery, driving her to the brink of madness with its unproductive, soul-destroying, energy-sapping trivialities. The real *emancipation of woman* and real communism begins where and when the mass struggle begins ... against these petty household chores and the true reforming of the masses into a vast socialist household.'

During the second half of the twenties, many towns published plans for building complexes consisting of schools, shops, laundries, nursery schools, etc. But there was no clear idea at this early stage of what the new society required. Two views emerged. Some architects believed that the basic format for a proletarian home was a small individual house with a Russian stove as opposed to the multi-storied flats of the bourgeoisie with their lifts and bathrooms. Others considered that the communal way of life which had grown up during the war years provided an ideal for the new housing plans.

Among the first projects for collective housing were those called 'communal homes' designed by the rationalists Ladovsky and Krinsky in 1920. Ladovsky's design was a complex multi-storied building, around a courtyard, broken into several blocks. Melnikov took part in a competition in 1923 to design show houses for workers in Moscow and created the first contemporarily significant communal house. This consisted of four living units joined on the second floor to a communal and social area by a covered corridor.

Many housing problems were worked on by the constructivists. In 1926, the journal *SA* organised a competition. The entries were shown at the exhibition of contemporary architecture held in Moscow to commemorate the tenth anniversary of the Revolution. These designs allowed a separate flat to each family, linked to a public area by corridors.

At that time there was much uncertainty how to structure communal housing. Only later did it become clear that the problem had been solved in the early days of Soviet rule. In designing communal homes the architects raised the problems of lightening the woman's tasks in the household, the socialisation of the unproductive part of everyday life, the organisation of the cultural leisure of the workers, etc.

Some projects proposed socialising all domestic aspects but most included besides the areas of cultural and social significance (ie the dining room, club, children's creche, laundry) flats for large families and rooms for those with small families. Many communal homes were built in Moscow, Leningrad, Tashkent, Baku and other towns. Unfortunately the conditions for their functioning satisfactorily as separate entities were upset, and the experiment was not carried out to its logical conclusion. Only in a few instances have they continued to function properly (eg the students, hostel in Moscow, built by I Nikolayev in 1930).

The work of a group of architects under Ginsburg broke new ground from 1928 to 1932 in a series of designs in which, for practically the first time, on a State level, the problems of the scientific organisation of domestic life were fully studied. Five experimental houses built in Moscow, Saratov and Sverdlovsk illustrated the new theory. The house on Tchaikovsky Street in Moscow aroused the greatest interest. Built in 1928–9 by Ginsburg and I Milinis it foresaw the idea of a single complex, consisting of four units: living, communal, domestic and a kindergarten. The project was not completely realised; only the living, the communal and a part of the domestic area were built. The living area consisted of several designs of flats, different only in height and the location of the inner staircase. A corridor on the second floor joined it to the communal area (a separate building) where the kitchen cum dining room (you could take your meals home) and the garden were situated.

The Vesnins about the same time designed a project for Kuznetsk of a living complex consisting of vast communal homes. Each one, accommodating 1,110 people, consisted of four living units, a social area, nursery schools and a boarding school. This project encouraged further interesting schemes from M Barschch and V Vladimirov (1929), I Golosov (1932) and others. Leonidov developed another way of relating living areas and communal institutions. In his project for a living complex in Magnitogorsk (1930) he proposed to place the apartments on free standing tower blocks and the social buildings on the edge of the complex, closer to the countryside.

In the 1920s attention was also paid to individual communal buildings such as shops, restaurants, public baths and schools, in order to improve cultural and basic amenities. Such institutions were often built with a view to serving large centralised buildings. In the large towns department stores were built on several floors, also factory kitchens with vast dining rooms catering for hundreds, and public baths with swimming pools, etc.

In almost every town and village, the spreading of socialist culture caused the development of workers' and village clubs, village reading rooms, national homes, palaces of workers, etc. The early workers' clubs were set up in former palaces and houses of the exploiting classes, but during the years of the civil war, planning had already started for the building of new club premises and gradually, in the 1920s, the workers' club emerged into Soviet architecture as a new type of public building. The clubs received a great amount of publicity, built as they were with the resources of the trade unions. They were built in many towns and villages. A special contribution was made by Melnikov who designed five clubs for Moscow; the Rusakov, the Gorky, the 'Kauchuk', the Frunze and the 'Stormy Petrel'.

Melnikov had worked on various new ways of making rooms multi-purpose. In this case he used sliding or rising partitions to divide the auditorium into separate areas, linked the auditorium and the sports section with sliding partitions, and could transform the auditorium into a swimming pool. Melnikov considered that the workers' clubs should reflect by their artistic appearance the new way of life of the workers. His inventive spirit is reflected in his concept of space, and even the most complicated of his planning ideas clearly defines the functional problems and is based on an exact spatial concept.

Workers' clubs and Houses of Culture were also built to designs submitted by the Vesnins (in Moscow and Baku), I Golosov (in Moscow), V Vladimirov (in Moscow), A Dmitriev (in Kharkov and Kramatorsk), A Gegello (in Leningrad) and others.

Leonidov introduced several new ideas into his projects for workers' clubs. Of special interest was his project for a Palace of Culture in the proletarian district in Moscow. This was an exploratory proposal to build a socio-cultural complex under the conditions demanded by a town of the future. Working on the assumption that a club should be a centre of social life, Leonidov allotted himself a vast area which he divided into four sectors each with a specific function. First a sector for physical culture and relaxation (stadium, sports grounds, an indoor swimming pool, a gymnasium). Secondly a sector for grandiose

Rodchenko's worker's club at the Paris Exhibitiion of Decorative Art 1925

events (an adaptable all-purpose hall with a large foyer). Thirdly an educational sector (museum, lecture halls). And lastly an exhibition hall.

Architects were faced early on with the task of designing buildings for the new government bodies. Houses of Soviets were intended by their very appearance to underline the national and democratic character of the socialist state and its local government bodies at any level. How difficult it was to find a convincing answer to this problem is shown by the divergent projects submitted by Zholtovsky and Ginsburg in a competition for the House of the Soviet in Makhachkala in 1926. Zholtovsky saw it as a vast pentagon with circular inner courtyards and with towers, Ginsburg as an open complex of separate units linked by passages. Ginsburg tried to emphasise the democracy of Soviet rule and its links with the people through the

composition of his government building. He showed the same approach in another competition project for Alma-Ata (1928). This was finished in 1930 and stands as the main building in the rebuilt social centre of the capital of Kazakhstan and now houses the State University of Kazakhstan.

New government centres were also built in the late twenties and early thirties in the capitals of other republics such as Kharkov (then capital of the Ukraine), Minsk and Erevan. Large assembly halls as the Dzerzhinsky Square in Kharkov and the government centre in Alma-Ata were acclaimed outside the Soviet Union. These were some of the first assembly halls to be built on such a large scale in the world and they demonstrated the potential of new architectural forms.

Barsch and Ginsburg

Soviet architecture had quickly covered a wide area of building theatres, schools, higher educational colleges, sports grounds, etc. Much of the work received world acclaim at that time, including the Vesnin's theatre in Kharkov which won the highest prize at the International competition in 1930, the dynamic exciting idea for a theatre in Rostov on Don, designed by V Shuko and V Gelfreich, 1930–35, the planetarium in Moscow (1927–29) where M Barschch and M Sinyavsky used several interesting devices: a parabolic cupola, a glazed spiral staircase and other things.

Town Planning

The decisive influence on Soviet town planning came from the industrialisation of the country – the key problem in the construction of socialism. During the civil war, work had already started on industrial and hydrotechnical buildings and it gained momentum during the first five year plan. The whole country was turned into a vast building site. Factories were built; electricity stations, mines, new towns arose close to sources of raw materials; new living complexes were built in old towns that already had heavy industrial enterprises. Urban populations quickly increased.

Barsch and Sinyavsky
Moscow Planetarium 1929

The Soviet architects were chiefly concerned with the difficulties of socialist resettlement and the planning of the expanding town. Professor Shestakov's project showed how he thought Greater Moscow should be allowed to develop. He proposed that Moscow should be expanded to 200,000 hectares, that the area should be carefully zoned (into industrial and park zones) and that two rings of satellite towns should be developed round Moscow, enveloping the existing towns and villages (the first ring 40–80 kilometres from Moscow and the second 90–120 kilometres away). Professor B Sakulin put forward a project in 1918 proposing that Moscow should be developed as the centre of an extensive economic area.

The headlong growth of towns in the nineteenth century forced the new planners to develop flexible plans allowing for free expansion while preserving the functional zones and without having to reconstruct the network of streets. Leonidov in his project for Magnitogorsk (1930) suggested developing a town along a main road (leading to an industrial zone) adding typical housing complexes and

Moscow Planetarium 1929

placing social, cultural, sporting, hospital, and other building parallel to the housing. However, because of the growth anticipation of a linear town, its new living areas would be further and further away from the place of work. Developing Leonidov's project further, N Milyutin in 1930 suggested his famous scheme, in which he placed industry parallel with the living area and with other functional zones (railway, green belt, main roads, etc). This allowed the town to develop without hindrance in both directions, but it did not allow for the building of effective social centres.

At the end of the 1920s Ladovsky became deeply involved with the problem of flexible planning. He analysed the merits and demerits of such schemes as linear and radial ring planning and as a result, in 1930, he worked on an essentially new scheme for planning an expanding town. This scheme could be considered either as coming in line with the mass produced functionalism of Milyutin's plan, or as breaking the radial ring system in one place. Ladovsky's plan shows a parabola in which a social centre develops along the axis, together with three zones, living, industrial and green belt. Ladovsky's scheme was rediscovered at the end of the fifties by the Greek architect K Doxiades.

There were also projects for using the space above the transport routes to form a second layer of town building. A Lavinsky designed a whole town where all the buildings were raised above the ground on springs (1921). Lissitsky in 1923–25 suggested building 'horizontal sky scrapers' above the intersections of the ring-like boulevards in Moscow with the mainly radial transport routes: two- or three-storey buildings built horizontally on high supports containing lifts and staircases. Melnikov designed a multi-storied car park for Paris (1925) to go on existing bridges over the Seine. These projects anticipated the proposals for vertical zoning in building.

The Change of Direction
A new architectural organisation was started in 1929 to stand beside ASNOVA and OSA. It was called VOPRA, the Union of Proletarian Architects. The formation of VOPRA coincided with the activities of two similar organisations in other fields of art RAPP (Russian Association of Proletarian Writers) and RAPKH (Russian Association of Proletarian Painters), whose supporters pressed for group restraint under the pretext of fighting for 'proletarian' art. The presence in VOPRA of a positive creative platform transferred the dispute to the field of scholastic quarrels over formulations and definitions. Having declared that the architectural trends of the constructivists and the rationalists were unproletarian (although the most influential architects of that time were either constructivists or rationalists) the supporters of VOPRA demanded the abandonment of vanguard positions in Soviet architecture. They sharply criticised eclecticism and stylisation and considered themselves on the extreme left in their search for a new architectural form. But in a competition to find a suitable project for a Palace of Soviets in Moscow which took place in the early 1930s they showed that in practice VOPRA could offer nothing to oppose archaic stylisation, eclecticism and ornamental monumentalism. The supporters of VOPRA in the end supported unmitigated eclectic stylisation and the use of compositional devices taken from the architecture of the past.

The competition for the Palace of Soviets stands at a turning point in the development in Soviet architecture. The two different approaches to the architectural concept of government institutions collided; their differences had already come to light in projects submitted in the 1920s (eg House of Government in Makhachkal, 1926). Should a public building be a monument in the traditional sense or a popular forum of contemporary design using a wide range of materials and construction methods?

At the beginning of the thirties, at a time when the new architecture was being realised with great authority, a direct return to the forms of the past in the project for the Palace of Soviets could not count on general recognition. All the same, the idea of conceiving a building intended to be the supreme government body of Soviet rule as a sort of monument triumphed at the competition and the plan of B Iofan, somewhat modernised, had great influence on the creative direction of Soviet architecture of the thirties to fifties by encouraging a tendency to ornate design. Later it was often said that the transition that many Soviet architects made in the 1930s into the 'decorative'

Zoltovsky
Power station Moscow 1927

period, showed above all that our building techniques were not ready for the very architecture which was prevailing in the 1920s. But there is only one, and to my mind, not very important reason why Soviet architecture changed direction in the early 1930s.

It would be wrong to deny the low standard of workmanship inherited from Tsarist Russia, but it was not as low as it was in some other fields of the national economy, which during the years of the first five-year plan swiftly reached world standards. There were many reasons why the building industry should not have developed more slowly than other branches of socialist industry.

In the twenties architecture put before the building industry the kind of tasks that helped it master the new building materials and designs and achieved a superior quality of construction. Engineering in the twenties in the building field gained significant results: see the metal constructions of V Shukhov, A Loleyt's work in reinforced concrete, the contemporary wooden constructions of G Karlsen, etc. For example, in 1922 Shukhov completed his radio station in Moscow which stood 150 metres high. At the beginning of the twenties work started on the Volkhovsky and Zemo-Archalsky hydro-electric power station and at the end of the twenties on the Dnieper hydro-electric scheme. During the years of the first five-year plan, architects actively took part in designing such gigantic socialist industrial schemes as the Chelyatinsk and the Stalingrad tractor works. Uralmash in Sverdlovsk, the car works in Gorky and the ball bearing factory in Moscow. These and many other engineering and industrial buildings were being built and materials and techniques were being developed concurrently. During the years of the first five-year plan there was great scope for new building factories and electricity stations, new towns and workers' settlements, thousands of homes, clubs, hospitals, sanatoria, schools, kindergartens and crèches, institutes, railway stations, etc. Socio-economic conditions favoured the development of architecture. Yet these conditions were not fully utilised by architects because of their uncritical attitude to their inheritance and their under-estimation of the role played by new structural techniques in forming an accepted style.

Right up to the middle of the 1930s it was difficult to detect in construction any serious change in the direction of Soviet architecture, so much so that many large buildings were completed which had been projected at the end of the twenties or in the early thirties: the theatre in Rostov on the Don (V Shchuko and V Gelfreich 1930–35), the *Pravda* offices in Moscow (P Golosov, 1929–35), the Palace of Culture for the Likhachev car works (Vesnins, 1932–37), the assembly hall of Dzerzhinsky in Square Kharkov (S Serafimov, S Kravets and others, 1925–34), the House of the Soviet in Minsk (I Langbard, 1932–35), the TSSU in Moscow (the former Centrosoyus, designed by Le Corbusier with N Kolli 1930–36) and others. Thus the first half of the 1930s saw a sharp struggle between two opposed views in Soviet architecture of our inheritance from the past.

Student of Ladovsky
Project for part of chemical works 1922

Architecture Statements Resolution on the Report of the House-Planning Section OSA (Association of Contemporary Architects)

Excerpt 1

At the All-Union meeting of the Association of Contemporary Architects, the members stressed the urgency of going over from projecting and constructing new dwellings on individual lines to new communal housing with a strict distribution of functions among individuals and communal groups, where courses for the maximum pooling and collectivisation of domestic duties will be made available to those concerned.

In this work, the new architect must do all he can to try and raise the standard of the dwellings with a view to furthering the organisation and development of domestic life on modern lines, whilst at the same time keeping building costs as low as possible and improving labour efficiency.

In the matter of planning, the haphazard building of new towns and the use of preconceived plans worked out blindly on the basis of a spot on the map or according to outdated ways of life has been contrasted with a detailed study of the functions of the town, not from the statistical angle, but as an entity in motion with all the possibilities for the utmost development of the town. Planning a new town is only possible after allowing for the factors that affect its character and role in the socialist reorganisation of the country. Work in finding materials and constructions which will ensure elasticity and enable the architects to replan the town and some of its edifices with as little inconvenience to its inhabitants as possible must also be taken into account.

Excerpt 2

Insofar as form is concerned, we categorically repudiate:

1 the ignorance of builders and engineers who are alien to matters of the socialist-artistic quality of architecture;

2 the unprincipled eclecticism of the 'embellishers' of architecture, who will readily dress up a piece of architecture whatever its social purpose in ready-made antiquated styles;

3 abstract hunting for a new form, unrelated to the social aims of a piece of architecture and without taking the actual possibilities of realising it into account;

4 naïve dilettantism of those wishing to symbolise this or that point of view by a decorative architectural form;

5 work in the so-called 'new style', using elements for 'contemporising' and embellishing old edifices.

We contrast all this with the organic growth of Soviet architecture, which is based on the specific features of a new social type and technically perfect construction methods.

Excerpt 3

Concerning the problems posed by new architecture in the West, we note elements that are akin to our own work among some of the more progressive Western architects, who have been influenced by the great world-wide advances in science and technology and by fine building methods. We also note the wide gulf between us insofar as the aims of architecture are concerned, which so clearly underlines the difference between the bourgeois social living conditions of the capitalist West and the new communal-domestic mutual relationships of a proletarian State that is engaged in building socialism.

Down with the speculator's art of 'prafs' and 'lefs'!

Down with the dilettante and amateurish attitude towards communal-artistic work!

Long live the materialistic school of artistic work, ie constructivism!

Excerpt 4

There exists a fairly widespread view that constructivism is artistic nihilism, ie that it denies form, is reluctant to take form into account. Actually, constructivism is a method of work that seeks to find the best and surest way towards a new form which will meet all the demands for the new socialist way of life. A sound aim of a communal collective, of a class – this is the star that guides us towards our goal; and since our work consists in creating material forms, we are by no means banning 'form', but instead affirm that we are approaching form by way of deploying a social aim. Form for us is a constant unknown quantity that keeps on being determined each time anew with reference to an aim, which is precisely defined in a revolutionary way.

'Contemporary Architecture' ('Sovremennaya Arkhitektura') 1928, No 5, pp 143–45

Kozlinsky Petrograd Rosta poster
The fist of the Revolution will crush the fist of the countryside
A slogan against the Kulaks
(Kulak = fist = profiteering peasant)

The Idiom of the Revolutionary Poster Edward Wright

After the October Revolution of 1917 in Russia, an immense quantity of posters appeared, and they varied also in their visual idiom (more than 3,000 are listed in 'Sovetskii Plakat', for the period 1918–1921). It is not surprising that we can recognise the flavour of expressionism, art nouveau or the rhetorical emphasis of the journalistic cartoon in many of them. The theme is revolutionary although in some cases the surviving conventions of calligraphic signatures, ornamental details and illusionistic representation remind us that here the visual language of a period is being used, not unlike that which was being used elsewhere for boosting commerce, recruitment and so forth. In September 1919, however, there appeared a new kind of poster, whose use is said to have been invented by Mikhail Cheremnykh, and known in the beginning as the 'Satire window of the Russian Telegraph Agency'. At this time the Russian Telegraph Agency had its name abbreviated to ROSTA (the equivalent of TASS today). Slogans, instructions, poetry were all in turn, boldly combined with graphic emblems and figuration, usually in sequence. The new idiom of the revolutionary poster is apparent, as it has become apparent during the last few years in the posters from Cuba.

Lubok Woodcut c 1725 How the mice buried the cat

Many of the ROSTA windows were by the artist and poet Mayakovsky, who provided pictures and text for at least nine of the very first series, at a time when the format was designed for each shop window individually with no duplication, numbers 1–21 (September 1919 till February 1920), consisted of 2, 3, 4 or more poster units of different content; the windows in which they were placed were the windows of empty shops and vacant business premises. A typical ROSTA structure would consist of 4, 6, 8, 12 or 14 narrative pictures and captions or verses applied by stencil. It might be worth noting that with serigraphy or silk-screen printing (the technique used for the Cuban posters) a more sophisticated stencilling technique is used on the colour screens. It is possible that the popular response to the narrative strip element of the ROSTA window may have grown from a familiarity with the 'lubok', a Russian picture-and-text, street literature, which survived until the beginning of this century. The ROSTA format for presenting information and instruction in political, military and economic matters appears as the revolutionary and environmental development of a typical

folk tradition. Camilla Gray, in *The Great Experiment: Russian Art 1863–1922*, mentions the influence of both the sacred ikon and the 'lubok' in the paintings of Goncharova and Larionov between 1908 and 1913. The author also states that: 'It was during this summer and the following year (1909) that the Burliuk brothers, following Larionov's example, began working in a style less identified with the French school, and with a growing interest in incorporating national folk-art traditions.' And later: 'David Burliuk made friends with Mayakovsky and together they began to devote themselves to poetry, both of them trying to incorporate the previous years' experience as painters.'...
With the Revolution the contours of 'poetry' or 'painting' became fused and integrated to give a new meaning to the environment (the street) or the transportation system (the railway).

After February 1920, simultaneously in different localities several copies of the more successful ROSTA posters were exhibited and identified by number (ROSTA N° XX). According to Cheremnych: 'The reproductions were carried out with lightning speed'; upon receipt of an original, there existed fifty copies by the following day, a few days later a whole edition (of 300 copies) would be completed. The stencil cutter usually worked with his family or a small 'collective' and the first copies to be made were immediately forwarded to the most distant ROSTA branches; those in the Moscow region being the last to receive their quota. Later on duplicate sets of cardboard stencils were forwarded on to the various localities to multiply the edition in that region once again. It was discovered that the emphatic numbering also maintained the expectation and interest of viewers who would inevitably look forward to the next poster to appear in that particular window, when its theme would be carried on and 'opened out like a window' as Wiktor Duwakin states in *ROSTAFENSTER – Majakowski als Dichter und bildender Künstler* (Dresden 1967). In connection with the 'window' concept of projecting information into the street, two designs for newspaper buildings (the *PRAVDA* project by A Vesnin and the *RADJANKO SELO* project for Kiev) both have glass screens, two floors in height, for a blown-up projection of the front page news, to be changed each day.

During the twenty-nine months from September 1919 until February of 1922 more than 1,600 different ROSTA posters appeared in their windows and in railway stations and other premises. The simple stencil-cut adaptability and team-work used to produce these narrative posters corresponded to the collective creative work on the 'Agit-prop' or Agitation-Instruction trains; in both cases projection or diffusion of revolutionary propaganda by every available technique was at the same time used to give a new semantic interpretation to an existing element of transition or transportation (window or railway train). That those who were making the Revolution should give a revolutionary baptism to environment and means of transportation was logical, insofar as a particular place or piece of rolling stock would be a reminder of the society which had produced it. In England social evolution occurs through metamorphosis; when something disappears suddenly, like the last tramway,

tears are shed (an Italian Futurist would find more poetry in the first tram's swaying movements). J V Stalin, in *Concerning Marxism in Linguistics* (Moscow 1950), has something to say about the semantics of the railway: 'At one time there were "Marxists" in our country who asserted that the railways left to us after the October Revolution were bourgeois railways, that it would be unseemly for us Marxists to utilise them, that they should be torn up and new "proletarian" railways built. For this they were nicknamed "troglodytes"... It goes without saying that such a primitive-anarchist view of society, of classes, of language has nothing in common with Marxism.'

Evgeni Zamyatin, in *On Literature, Revolution and Entropy* (Moscow 1924), emphasises the nature of creative renewal when he states: 'The broad highway of Russian literature, worn shiny by the giant wheels of Tolstoy, Gorky, Chekhov, is realism, real life; consequently we must turn away from real life. The rails, sanctified and canonised by Blok, Sologub, Bely, are the rails of symbolism – symbolism which turned away from real life; consequently we must turn toward real life.

Absurd, isn't it? The intersection of parallel lines is also absurd. But it is absurd only in the canonical, plane geometry of Euclid; in non-Euclidian geometry it's an axiom.'

An idiom changes within a historical context, accumulating its new words and images, frequently rediscovering others in its popular linguistic tradition, to correspond to the new situation; in this process it discards those which are obsolete. J L Borges, in *The Speech of Buenos Aires*, comments on this and says: 'The English language has not been pushed into a corner by slang,' and elsewhere: 'the "wealth" of a language can be a euphemistic term for its death.' The first phase of the revolutionary poster idiom in Russia was typified by the ROSTA pattern, corresponding in execution and distribution to the immense creative effort of propaganda and education carried out during the civil war.

The phase which followed was typified by montage, technical experiment and the work of Lissitzky, Rodchenko, Klutsis and others. In the *New Left Review*, N° 41, an essay on 'The Future of the Book' by El Lissitzky conveys some idea of the creative climate of these first two phases of the Revolution: 'The new movement which began in Russia in 1908 bound painter and poet together from the very first day . . . they did not produce select, numbered, de luxe editions, but cheap unlimited volumes, which today we must treat as popular art despite their sophistication.

In the Revolutionary period a latent energy has concentrated in the younger generation of our artists, which can only find release in large-scale popular commissions. The audience has become the masses, the semi-literate masses. With our work the Revolution has achieved a colossal labour of propaganda and enlightenment. We ripped up the traditional book into single pages, magnified these a hundred times, printed them in colour and stuck them up as posters in the streets . . . ours were not designed for rapid perception from a passing motor-car, but to be read and to enlighten from a short distance.' Three paragraphs further on he writes that: 'With the advent of the period of reconstruction in 1922, the production of books also rose rapidly. Our best artists seized on the problem of book production. At the beginning of 1922, I and the writer Ilya Ehrenburg edited the periodical *Vesch-Gegenstand-Objet* which was printed in Berlin. Access to the most developed German printing techniques enabled us to realise some of our ideas about the book. Thus we printed a picture-book *The Story of Two Squares* . . . and the Mayakovski-Book . . .'

In the phase of reconstruction, the idiom of the poster captured attention by its dynamism, but demanded a more sophisticated awareness of the creative climate. It showed its affinity with the new typographic design of books and exhibitions, with architectural structure, theatre design and with the techniques of the cinema. Even before the unequalled creative genius of S M Eisenstein became known, a group directed by Dziga Vertov had published a manifesto in 1919 in support of the documentary film, outlining the principles of what is now called 'cinéma-vérité', and at that time known as 'cinéma-œuil' by those who received it favourably in Paris. The athletic games poster 'Spartakiada' by G Klutsis (1928) synchronises by its montage of documentary photography and text, recreating an event, as would be done by the montage in the diachronic structure of a film. Two posters by the brothers Stenberg, for the Buster Keaton film *The General* and *Earth* by Dovchenko, make use of symbolic resonance rather than dynamic structure. In these two posters figuration and sign are combined to recall the tradition of the Russian ikon.

Peter and Mary Mayer have helped in the documentation of this text.

Stenberg brothers poster

Klutsis 1928

Stenberg brothers poster
Springtime

Stenberg brothers
The General (Buster Keaton)

Re-enactment of the storming of the Winter Palace

The Storming of the Winter Palace

Two weeks before 7 November 1920 there appeared over the gates of the Winter Palace a sign 'Headquarters Organiser of October Celebrations', and the entrance, vestibule and ground floor of what is now the Museum of the Revolution sprang to life with an unusual kind of activity. Sentries, passes, the noise of vehicles, signs with 'Communications', 'Transport', 'OC Headquarters': everything indicated a big organisation set up for some urgent and complex event. Early each morning a messenger or telephone call would wake somebody or other involved in the theatre to inform him that he had been mobilised to take part in a mass spectacle in Uritsky Square. From first thing in the morning a queue of people stood waiting at the entrance to the Headquarters: drama schools, theatre studios and clubs en bloc, representatives of military units, detachments of Red soldiers and sailors. This vast horde of manpower was sorted out in a special allocation section and everyone was given work appropriate to his qualifications in the task of staging *The Storming of the Winter Palace*. Building materials were delivered to the Square; in front of the Headquarters by Red Army Arch and the Party Executive Committee offices there were mountains of boards, planks and laths, boxes of nails, endless coils of wire. An army of carpenters hammered away, erecting huge platforms in front of the two wings of the buildings which enclose the most amazing Square in the world. In front of the Military Commissariat was built a multi-storey stand, by the Alexander Column a tall command tower, and before the main gates of the Palace were huge stacks of timber just as there had been on 7 November 1917. By night the work continued without pause in the light of searchlights.

... Dozens of producers, writers, stage-designers and technicians worked out an overall scenario for the production, splitting it into five parts: 'White', 'Red', 'Bridge', 'Square' and 'Palace'. The White part consisted of scenes performed on the 'White' platform, that is, scenes concerning the Provisional Government, the Kerensky period, the war, and the disintegration of the old army. The Red part consisted of scenes performed against a background representing huge factories, and dealt with the bolshevisation of the masses, their activities in the days preceding October, their mobilisation, and the forming of the Red Guards. The 'Bridge' was a real bridge which joined the 64 metre long Red and White platforms, a junction between two worlds, two groups – the Kerenskyites and the Bolsheviks. 'The Square' was reserved for the immense battle scene: the assault on the Winter Palace by the people and the insurgent troops who entered through Red Army Arch from the direction of Pevchesky Bridge, Million Street and Workers' Gardens.

... The intended scale of the performance ruled out any scenes dealing with individual characters. The entire action was condensed into group movements, animated tableaux and dynamic crowd scenes. The masses were treated as masses. The sole exception was the small figure of Kerensky, which served to emphasise his insignificant role in the events as they were unfolded. More than anywhere else the Alexander Hall was snowed under with work: the original nucleus of participants acquired more and more layers as time went on and by the day of the dress-rehearsal on the Square there were 10,000 present.

The triumphal procession of Kerensky and his associates greeted by the clergy, the bourgeoisie, the Junkers, the Women's Batallion, etc, the fever of speculation which followed the 'Freedom Loan', the despatch of more and more detachments of 'cannon fodder' to the front (one recalls the stirring marching songs sung by Red soldiers who had actually served in the war), the procession of the victims of the imperialist carnage, and alternating with this the working masses greeting their returning leaders, the first angry speeches and the first reverses – it was all combined to produce a single great panoramic review, filled with satire, tragic fervour and historic grandeur.

'We give freedom'
scene from the *Storming of the Winter Palace* 1920

A group of young composers wrote the music which was played by a huge orchestra under the direction of Hugo Varlikh. Army instructors taught young girls from theatre studios marching and rifle drill in order that they could play the Women's Battalion. Hundreds of morning suits, top hats, Generals' uniforms and ball gowns were obtained for the actors on the 'white' platform. The Red Army was busy setting up field artillery batteries in Workers' Gardens. The producers, their assistants and everybody else on the production side worked round the clock, living on kasha, tea and frozen apples.

The searchlights installed on the roofs of the buildings surrounding the square lit up the area of action, and one after another, like the episodes in a film, the scenes began to unfold on the Red and White platforms. From the command tower signals were issued by telephone, using a numbered code to refer to the various episodes. Right up to the moment when the troops at the front rebelled and when the masses on the Red platform invaded the White the action developed just as it might have done in the theatre. But the moment when the signal rocket sped up from the Square and exploded in the night sky the spectators and the participants too witnessed one of the most astonishing sights imaginable, a sight which burst the narrow confines of the traditional stage, and rose above those earthbound planks, boldly mixing recent reality with a vivid, audacious, theatricalised interpretation of that reality on a scale hitherto undreamed of.

K N DERZHAVIN
Zhizn iskusstva, 1925, No 45
translated by Edward Braun

Constructivism in
the Theatre
Edward Braun

In 1918 towns throughout Soviet Russia were
decorated to celebrate the first anniversary
of the October Revolution. The ancient
monuments of Petrograd were transformed
by the brash geometrical designs of Nathan
Altman and his comrades of the artistic Left.
All over the capital theatrical groups performed
agitatory shows in soldiers', workers' and
students' clubs, whilst in Moscow the occasion
was marked by the presentation of *A Pantomime
of the Great Revolution*, the first of the mass
spectacles. However in those days of political
instability the professional theatre still maintained a position of cautious neutrality, and
largely ignored the Bolshevik government's
exhortations to join in its celebrations. In
Petrograd the only truly revolutionary contribution was a production by Vsevolod Meyerhold
of *Mystery-Bouffe*, Mayakovsky's allegory of
the triumph of the international proletariat.
This alliance of 'Futurists', as they were
loosely termed, was completed by the Suprematist painter Malevich, who designed the settings
and costumes in what he later described as
'Cubist terms':

> I saw the box-stage as the frame of a picture
> and the actors as contrasting elements (in
> Cubism every object is a contrasting element
> in relation to another object). Planning the
> action on three or four levels, I tried to deploy
> the actors in space predominantly in vertical
> compositions in the manner of the latest
> style of painting; the actors' movements
> were meant to accord rhythmically with the
> elements of the setting. I depicted a number
> of planes on a single canvas; I treated space
> not as illusionary but as cubist. I saw my task
> not as the creation of associations with a
> reality existing beyond the limits of the stage,
> but as the creation of a new reality.[1]

None of Malevich's designs survive, but eye-
witness accounts suggest that the escape
from external reality was not complete, that
there remained clear allusions to concrete
objects. Even so the treatment of scenic space
was bold and anticipated much that was to
come. Quite apart from its profound political
significance, *Mystery-Bouffe* was more
advanced than Malevich's earlier designs for
the 1913 Petersburg production of Kruchenikh's
opera, *Victory over the Sun*, to which Malevich
ascribed the birth of Suprematist painting.
For all the originality of the costumes and
backdrops and their personal significance for
the artist, that work remained just one more
example of actors moving on a flat stage
against a two-dimensional painted background,
and as theatre was relatively unimportant.[2]

After *Mystery-Bouffe* no further Soviet work
was staged in any professional theatre until
the same play was revived by Meyerhold in
Moscow in 1921. Meanwhile the advancement
of revolutionary drama was left to the countless
new amateur theatre clubs which sprang up
throughout the Republic and to the organisers
of the mass performances which were staged
outdoors in many major cities on the occasions
of national holidays. These performances
usually depicted events from recent revolutionary history, but in their exploitation of stirring
spectacle and theatrical effects interspersed
with broad knockabout humour they were a
direct extension of the ancient traditions of
popular religious festivals and street
processions.

[2] For accounts of *Victory over the Sun* see Camilla
Gray, *The Great Experiment: Russian Art 1863 – 1922*
(London, 1962), p 308

[1] Quoted by A Fevralsky in A Anastasev and
E Peregudova (ed), *Spektakli i gody* (Moscow, 1969), p 12

The Storming of the Winter Palace, re-enacted on the third anniversary and at the actual scene of the event in Petrograd, involved over 6,000 participants plus the cruiser Aurora on the nearby Neva, and was watched by a crowd of over 100,000. Produced by Nikolai Evreinov, Alexander Kugel and Nikolai Petrov with designs by Yury Annenkov, it was organised by Dmitri Temkin.

Such performances became less frequent after the Civil War, but they did much to influence the form of early Soviet propagandist theatre, in particular its handling of documentary material, its lampooning of capitalist archetypes, and its frequent recourse to startling sound and visual effects.[3]

[3] See account of *The Earth in Turmoil*, p 73

Initially, however, the professional stage remained aloof from such vulgarity and the repertoires of Stanislavsky, Nemirovich-Danchenko, Vakhtangov, Tairov and others abounded in the works of such dramatists as Claudel, Scribe, Gozzi, Maeterlinck, Oscar Wilde and Lord Byron. The prevailing attitude was summed up by Tairov in December 1920 when he said: 'A propagandist theatre after a revolution is like mustard after a meal.'[4]

[4] Quoted in *Vestnik teatra*, Moscow, 1920, No 78–79, p 16

The Storming of the Winter Palace

The task of relating the theatre to Soviet reality was entrusted to Meyerhold. In the autumn of 1920 Lunacharsky, the Commissar for Education, recalled him from service with the Red Army to take charge of the Commissariat's Theatre Department with power over the entire Soviet Federation. Meyerhold's response was characteristically dramatic: under the banner of 'October in the Theatre' he announced the mobilisation of all theatrical resources, starting with the reorganisation of the so-called 'academic theatres', amongst them the Moscow Art, the Kamerny, the Maly, and the former Alexandrinsky in Petrograd. His eventual aim was a complete network of 'RSFSR Theatres', but in the event only his own, the RSFSR Theatre No 1 in Moscow came to anything. His demolition plans were firmly resisted by the government, which reasoned that traditional works and production techniques merited preservation, and in any case were probably far more comprehensible to the masses than the revolutionary innovations of the Futurists.

Meyerhold was forced to resign after barely four months in office, but he did achieve two productions at the RSFSR No 1 which were crucial in the development of the Soviet theatre. The first was *The Dawn* (Les Aubes), Verhaeren's epic verse drama of world revolution; it was hurriedly adapted by Meyerhold and his assistant Bebutov to give it specific relevance to recent events and presented on 7 November 1920 to mark the third anniversary of the October Revolution.

The derelict, unheated auditorium of the former Sohn Theatre with its flaking plaster and broken seats was more like a meeting-hall, but this was wholly appropriate for it was in the spirit of a political meeting that Meyerhold conceived the production. Admission was free, the walls were hung with hortatory placards, and the audience was showered at intervals with leaflets. Also derived from the meeting was the declamatory style of the actors, who mostly remained motionless and addressed their speeches straight at the

The Dawn

audience. Critics compared the production with Greek tragedy, which furnished the precedent for the static manner of delivery and for the chorus in the orchestra pit commenting on the peripeteia of the drama. The chorus was assisted in the task of guiding and stimulating audience reaction by a claque of actors concealed throughout the auditorium. At a fixed point in the play the character of the Herald would enter and deliver a bulletin on the progress of the real Civil War in the South. Meyerhold's highest aspirations were gratified on the night when the Herald announced the decisive break into the Crimea at the Battle of Perekop and the entire theatre rose in a triumphant rendering of the *Internationale*. Such unanimity of response did not occur every night but usually only when military detachments attended en bloc – as they sometimes did, complete with banners flying and bands ready to strike up.

Whilst the more sophisticated specatator was likely to find the conventions crude and the acting maladroit – not to mention the political message oversimplified or even repugnant – the proletariat at whom ostensibly the production was aimed could not help but be puzzled by its appearance. The young designer, Vladimir Dmitriev, constructed a setting of three-dimensional shapes similar to the early 'reliefs' by Tatlin; but the assembly of red, gold and silver cubes, discs and cylinders, cut-out tin triangles and intersecting ropes blended uneasily with the occasional recognisable object such as a graveyard cross or the gates of a city, to say nothing of the soldiers' spears and shields or the curious 'timeless' costumes of daubed canvas. Furthermore the overall picture was made to look tawdry in the harsh white light with which Meyerhold sought to dispel all illusion.

But for all its imperfections, *The Dawn* was a major success with the public, running for well over a hundred performances to packed houses. In his attempt to unite performers and spectators in a common experience, Meyerhold brought into the theatre something of the spirit of the mass spectacles and, if for this reason alone, *The Dawn* must be regarded as a *locus classicus* in the history of the political theatre.

The proscenium which had been bridged by the use of the orchestra pit in *The Dawn* was demolished once and for all in Meyerhold's revival of *Mystery-Bouffe* for May Day 1921 (setting by Lavinsky and Khrakovsky). The stage proper was occupied by a series of platforms of varying levels, interconnected by steps and vaguely suggestive of the various locations of the action. In front a broad ramp sloped right down to the first row of seats, bearing a huge hemisphere over which the cast clambered and which revolved to expose the exit from 'Hell'. In this scene one of the devils was played by a circus clown, Vitaly Lazarenko, who entered by sliding down a wire and performed acrobatic tricks. In the final act, which depicted the new *electrified* promised land, the action spilled into the boxes adjacent to the stage and at the conclusion the audience was invited to mingle with the actors onstage.

Mystery-Bouffe

In this production Meyerhold dispensed finally with a front curtain and flown scenery. The theatre was bursting at the seams, unable to accommodate the kind of popular spectacle which he was striving to achieve. It was now that the questions arose whose answers were shortly to be sought in Constructivism.

The only experimental theatre to survive the Revolution was the Kamerny Theatre, founded by Tairov in 1914. More than any other director Tairov appreciated the significance of the Futurist movement in painting. Larionov, Goncharova, Exter, and Yakulov all worked with him as stage-designers at a time when Meyerhold was continuing his almost exclusive association with Alexander Golovin of the 'World of Art' at the Petersburg Imperial Theatres.

Perhaps the most successful of Tairov's designers at this time was Alexandra Exter. For the production of Annensky's Grecian tragedy *Famira the Lyrist* in 1916 they jointly devised a setting whose cubes, pyramids and sloping planes both echoed the hills and cypress trees of a Hellenic landscape and furnished a series of levels which enhanced the plasticity of the actor's body in motion, serving as 'a flexible and obedient keyboard with the aid of which he could exercise his creative freedom to the greatest possible extent'.[5]

Famira the Lyrist

As early as 1907 in his work with Vera Komissarzhevskaya Meyerhold had found inspiration in Adolphe Appia's revolutionary treatment of scenic space and his use of lighting to enhance the expressive power of the actor's body.[6] Tairov, both in *Famira* and in later productions, was motivated by the same ideas. The later links of the two Russian directors with artistic developments in their own country should not be allowed to obscure the fact that the influence of the great Swiss pioneer probably penetrated earlier and deeper in Russia than in any other country.

[5] A Tairov, *O Teatre* (Moscow, 1970), p 167

[6] See E Braun, *Meyerhold on Theatre* (London, 1969), Sections 1 and 2

In 1921 Tairov interpreted *Romeo and Juliet* as a 'symphony of bold and passionate, mighty and consuming, cruel and splendid erotic power'.[7] Exter designed stylised costumes and a practicable non-representational setting on seven levels which together furnished an ideal medium for the expression of the drama's violent action. In appearance the result was reminiscent of Rayonnist painting with its 'spatial forms ... obtained through the crossing of reflected rays from various objects, and forms which are singled out by the artist'.[8] But in principle the production remained close to *Famira the Lyrist* five years before.

[7] A Tairov, op cit p 290

[8] Camilla Gray, op cit pp 124–5

Romeo and Juliet

Closer still perhaps was the Kamerny's version of Racine's *Phèdre* (1922) with designs by the Constructivist architect Alexander Vesnin.

As usual with Tairov, the setting expressed reality in an artistic, somewhat symbolic form. The stage resembled a sort of sloping deck; orange and red cloths reminded you of sails. According to Tairov, the sloping stage signified, prompted the sensation of an impending inner catastrophe. It represented not only the alarming list of a ship's deck at the point of disaster but also the heeling over of the spirit. The cylinders deployed to either side of the stage lent weight to the scenic composition, completed the picture. The setting was most receptive to light, and moments of spiritual alarm were emphasised by lighting changes. Tairov honoured the tradition of French classicism by keeping the stage empty of all furniture. Whilst the actors seemed to be allowed total freedom, the breaks in the stage level (there were variations in height apart from the overall slope) enabled the director to mould the actors into almost sculptural forms. Tairov had discovered the secret of moving the human form in open space. Those spare movements could seem elementary at first glance. They were precise and few in number, but they had a kind of geometrical harmony. Tairov did not discard the laws of French classicism; rather he extracted from them a fertile theatrical seed.[9] (Pavel Markov).

In 1923 Tairov took his company to Germany and France where *Phèdre* was a sensational success. Cocteau called it a masterpiece and Fernand Léger wrote to Tairov 'I assure you that there is nothing in Paris to compare with this ... My dream is to tackle the problem of plasticity on the stage as you have done.'[10] Tairov achieved nothing finer than *Phèdre*, but although Lunacharsky called it 'the first great stride towards true monumental art',[11] it was essentially a product of pre-revolutionary culture, a work inspired by traditional idealism.

Phèdre

Phèdre

Phèdre

[9] In A Tairov, op cit p 21

[10] Letter dated 9 March 23, ibid, p 543

[11] A Lunacharsky, *O teatre i dramaturgii* (Moscow, 1958), vol 1, p 411

In his *Notes of a Director* published in 1921 Tairov significantly heads the chapter on stage setting 'Stage Atmosphere'. This accurately conveys his conception of the role of design in the theatre: it is neither a naturalistic representation of reality nor simply a means of enhancing the actor's performance; it is part of a total theatrical synthesis which conveys the atmosphere, the inner mood of the action. To do this it may employ symbolic means (like the listing deck in *Phèdre*) or allusions of external reality (the cypress trees in *Famira*) but they remain subordinated to the ultimate, *atmospheric* purpose. To describe this style Tairov coined the term 'Neo-Realism', meaning an emotional realism whose form was determined exclusively by the particular pattern of emotions and limited only by the peculiar properties of the theatre.[12]

In the autumn of 1921 Meyerhold became Director of the newly formed State Higher Theatre Workshop in Moscow. It was there that he developed the system of practical exercises for actors called Biomechanics and based, he claimed, on recent experiments in the scientific organisation of labour in America and Russia. There seems little doubt that Meyerhold gave his system this fashionable 'industrial' colouring in order to discredit the rival methods of Stanislavsky and Tairov, which he dismissed as unscientific and anachronistic. But this need not detract from the intrinsic value of Biomechanics as a means of fostering physical discipline and self-awareness in the actor. The system of twenty dramatised solo and group exercises, many of them derived from traditional circus and commedia dell'arte stunts, became indispensible to the dynamic style of theatre which Meyerhold now developed.

The first production in which it was demonstrated was Fernand Crommelynck's tragifarce, *The Magnanimous Cuckold*, presented by Meyerhold and his students in April 1922. As he himself recalls, circumstances had forced him to seek a setting which could be erected anywhere, without resorting to conventional stage machinery.[13] Having worked

already with two Constructivist designers, Vesnin and Lyubov Popova, on an unrealised project for a mass performance called *Struggle and Victory* in April 1921, Meyerhold now found the solution to his problem at the first Constructivist exhibition which opened under the title *5 × 5 = 25* in Moscow late in the same year. In their constructions Meyerhold saw the possibility of a utilitarian, multi-purpose scaffolding which could easily be dismantled and re-erected in any surroundings. Furthermore, like Biomechanics this industrial 'anti-art' which recognised practicability as its sole criterion and condemned all that was merely depictive or decorative, seemed to him a natural ally in his repudiation of naturalism and aestheticism.

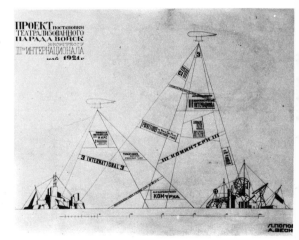

Struggle and Victory

[12] For an English translation see *Notes of a Director* (trans W Kuhlke), University of Miami, 1969

[13] See *The Magnanimous Cuckold*, p 81 of this catalogue

The Magnanimous Cuckold

At Meyerhold's invitation Popova joined the staff of the Theatre Workshop and agreed to build a construction for *The Magnanimous Cuckold*. It consisted of the frames of conventional theatre flats and platforms joined by steps, chutes and catwalks; there were two wheels, a large disc bearing the letters 'CR-ML-NK', and vestigial windmill sails, which all revolved at varying speeds as a kinetic accompaniment to the fluctuating passions of the characters. Blank panels hinged to the framework served as doors and windows. The characters wore loose-fitting blue overalls with only the odd distinguishing mark such as a pair of red pom-poms, an eye-glass or a riding crop. But despite the skeletal austerity, the grimy damp-stained brickwork of the exposed back wall and the absence of wings to hide either stage-crew or cast, Popova's contraption evoked inevitable associations with the windmill in which the play was originally set, suggesting now a bedroom, now a balcony, now the grinding mechanism, now a chute for sacks of flour. Only in the isolated moments when it enhanced the synchronised movements of the complete ensemble did it work simply as a functional machine. In the theatre, whose whole allure depends on the associative power of the imagination, every venture by the Constructivists led to an unavoidable compromise of their utilitarian dogma and each time demonstrated the inherent contradiction in the term 'Theatrical Constructivism'.

But for all the solecisms of Popova's setting in the eyes of the Constructivists, it proved the ideal platform for a display of biomechanical agility and the potentionally salacious bedroom-farce plot was completely redeemed by the brio and good humour of the production. Furthermore, it was, so to speak, the public debut of Constructivism, for the Moscow exhibition had been a display of early laboratory experiments which marked the final rejection of easel-painting and the assumption by the group of a purely utilitarian role. Following Popova, the majority of the group abandoned their antipathy towards the theatre and Constructivism became the dominant trend in stage design.

The Magnanimous Cuckold

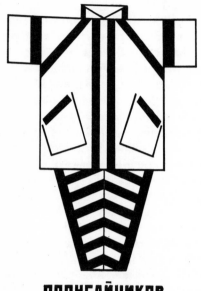

ПОПУГАЙЧИКОВ

ТАРЕЛКИН

ДЕТИ

БРАНДАХЛЫСТОВА

In November 1922 *The Magnanimous Cuckold* was joined in Meyerhold's repertoire by *Tarelkin's Death*, Sukhovo-Kobylin's nineteenth-century satire on Tsarist police methods. The designer was Varvara Stepanova, Rodchenko's wife and like Popova a participant in the $5 \times 5 = 25$ exhibition.

In a note to the play the author writes 'In keeping with the work's humorous nature it must be played briskly, merrily, loudly – *avec entrain*.' This prompted Meyerhold to employ once again the knockabout tricks of circus clowns and strolling players. Stepanova designed a series of baggy costumes decorated with stripes, patches and chevrons. On the bare stage there was an assortment of white-painted 'acting instruments' ready to be shifted and used by the actors as required. Each one concealed a trap: the table's legs gave way, the seat deposited its occupant on the floor, the stool detonated a blank cartridge. Most fearsome of all was the cage used to simulate a prison cell into which the prisoner was fed

head first through something resembling a giant meat-mincer. As though all this was not enough to the spectator's nerves and the actor's courage, an assistant director (or 'laboratory assistant' as they were called) announced the intervals by firing a pistol at the audience and shouting 'Entrrr-acte!'. Illusion was given no chance to intrude: old women were played by young men, there were helter-skelter chases with the pursuers brandishing bladders on sticks, and at the end Tarelkin escaped by swinging across the stage on a trapeze.

But for all the production's vigour and invention it failed to share the success of *The Magnanimous Cuckold*. Mainly it was marred by practical faults: the capricious functioning of the 'acting instruments' shattered the nerves of the young performers; the shapeless costumes tended to camouflage rather then enhance their movements; and they frequently had to perform in half-darkness due to an inadequate lighting system.

Enough Simplicity in Every Wise Man

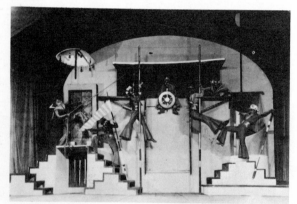

The Earth in Turmoil

Nevertheless *Tarelkin's Death* remains one of the most celebrated products of the movement known as 'Eccentrism' which flourished in Russia in the early twenties, restoring pure clowning to the stage and equally influencing the comic style of the new Soviet cinema.

One of Meyerhold's two 'laboratory assistants' for the production was a pupil from the Theatre Workshop, Sergei Eisenstein. Shortly afterwards he left to work as a director at the Moscow Proletkult Theatre, and it was there that in 1923 he staged Ostrovsky's *Enough Simplicity in Every Wise Man* as a 'montage of attractions' on an arena stage and complete with a tightrope act by one of the characters.

As often as not 'Eccentrism' was exploited for the purpose of political satire, but Tairov made no such claim for his production of Lecocq's operatta *Girofle-Girofla* which was presented a month before *Tarelkin's Death*. He drew on all the tricks of the circus and the music-hall to produce a light-hearted spectacle which dazzled Moscow and quite disarmed orthodox criticism. In contrast to his recent monumental *Phèdre* the atmosphere created by *Girofle-Girofla* was one of sheer high spirits which owed everything to the theatre and little or nothing to social or psychological truth. The effect owed much to Georgy Yakulov's setting which was as starkly utilitarian as anything by the most doctrinaire Constructivist:

> The whole installation was treated more as an instrument for acting than as any real, defined location, even though all its details hinted at a 'maritime atmosphere'. It was, so to speak, a living setting in which hatches opened and shut and objects came on and left the stage of their own accord, and only to the extent that they were useful to the actors. They served as instruments for him, as what might be called the tools of his trade.[14]

As early as the beginning of 1923 Ivan Aksenov wrote:

> So-called stage constructivism started with a most impressive programme for the total abolition of aesthetic methods, but once it appeared on the stage it began to show signs of being only too ready to adapt itself to its

[14] P Markov in A Tairov, op cit p 24

surroundings and now it has degenerated almost to a decorative device, albeit in a new style.[15]

Two months later Meyerhold staged *The Earth in Turmoil*, an adaptation by Sergei Tretyakov of Martinet's *La Nuit* which tells of an abortive mutiny during an imaginary imperialist war. Like *The Dawn* it was altered to incorporate direct allusions to recent Soviet history.

In an attempt to eliminate all risk of aesthetic blandishments, Meyerhold and his designer, Popova, resorted to purely utilitarian objects: cars, lorries, motor cycles, machine-guns, harvester – only that which was required by the dramatic events. The one exception was a huge stark wooden gantry-crane which towered up into the flies. The sole sources of light were giant front-of-house military search-lights. The costumes were wholly naturalistic and the actors wore no make-up. At one point in the action a lorry drove down the gangway of the auditorium bearing the coffin of a martyred Red soldier.

The Earth in Turmoil was conceived in the spirit of a mass spectacle and was performed on a number of occasions in the open air with the setting freely adapted to the surroundings. In June 1924 it was presented in Moscow with the participation of infantry and horse cavalry and before an audience of 25,000.

Aksenov's diagnosis of the metamorphosis of Constructivism proved all too accurate: in the mid-twenties many theatres, both in the Soviet Union and elsewhere, exploited it as the latest fashionable decorative device, often with little regard for the play's content. But what it was sometimes used to express most aptly in a half symbolic, half representational manner was the breakneck tempo of life in the big city and the dehumanising effects of the machine age. Meyerhold, Tairov, and many lesser Soviet directors staged hurriedly written plays, updated adaptations, and revues (like the Kamerny's *Kukirol* in 1925) satirising the Western way of life but often betraying distinct nostalgia for its decadent attactions.

The Earth in Turmoil

Kukirol

[15] *Zrelishcha*, Moscow, 1923, No 21, p 8

Lake Lyul

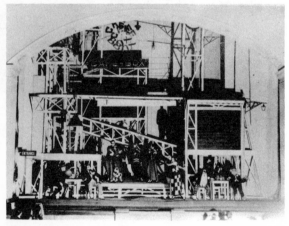

The Man who was Thursday

Meyerhold's productions of *Lake Lyul* by Alexei Faiko and Tairov's adaptation of Chesterton's novel, *The Man who was Thursday*, both staged at the beginning of the 1923–24 season, were outstanding examples of the genre. Both used highly complex constructions (designed by Victor Shestakov and Alexander Vesnin respectively) of several storeys with lifts, stairs, advertisement hoardings and screens for projected titles. With the help of area lighting both productions employed a rapid sequence of episodes in a manner resembling montage at a time when that technique had been scarcely explored in the cinema.

This mastery of tempo, spatial flexibility, and a readiness to disregard traditional stage configurations is characteristic of most of the best Soviet theatre in the twenties. The setting was reduced to a structural minimum: given only the art of the actor, a few props, and freed from the need for any verisimilitude, it could be as little as the curving staircase for Selvinsky's *Commander of the Second Army* (designed by Meyerhold and Sergei Vakhtangov) or the sloping platform for Ostrovsky's *Storm* (by the Stenberg brothers and Medunetsky for Tairov).

Commander of the Second Army

Storm

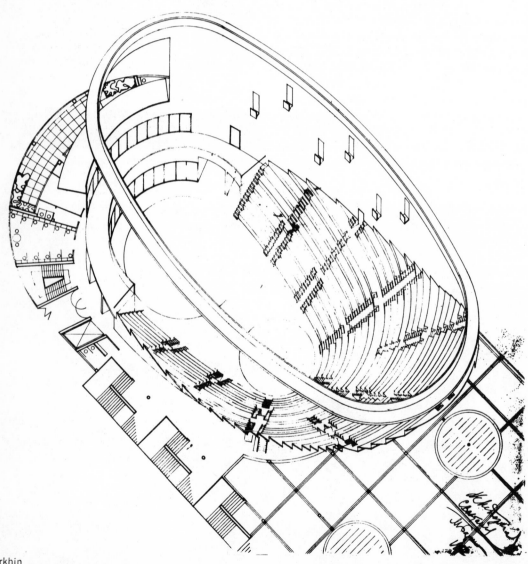

Barkhin
Project for the Meyerhold Theatre 1932

Productions like these demonstrated the total irrelevance of the proscenium arch and the logic of the open stage or theatre in the round. As the designs for the theatre built to his specification show,[16] Meyerhold for one was well aware of this; but he never lived to see its completion and his work was robbed of its natural conclusion. There remains the joint project with Lissitzky for Tretyakov's *I Want a Child* (1927–30), a bold attempt to transform an inadequate auditorium and a tantalising glimpse of what Meyerhold might have achieved in a building worthy of his genius.

[16] Architects M Barkhin and S Vakhtangov

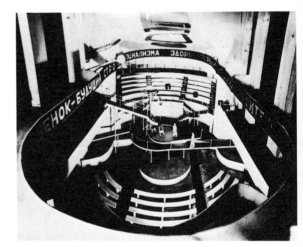

I want a Child

Mystery-Bouffe

No matter how hard all the various theatres might try to choose the best possible plays to mark the anniversary, they are not likely to find anything in the ancient treasure-house of mankind which will really satisfy our new demands. Of course, it will be splendid to see Romain Rolland's *Storming of the Bastille; William Tell*, both in Schiller's original version and enhanced by Rossini's music, is more or less in accord with our feelings; there will be a whole series of other productions: *Brand*, Galsworthy's *Strife*, and so on. This is all very well, but it seems to me that the only play which owes its conception to our Revolution and which therefore conveys its spirit, its lively, audacious, buoyant, challenging spirit, is Mayakovsky's *Mystery-Bouffe*.

Obviously I cannot guarantee its success, having only read it and heard it read by the author. As a work of literature it is most original, powerful and beautiful. But how it will turn out in production I don't yet know. I am very much afraid that the Futurists might have made millions of mistakes. But Futurism has one splendid feature: it is a young and bold movement. And in so far as its best members have greeted the Communist Revolution with open arms, they are more likely than anybody else to become the virtuoso drummers of our Red culture. But at the same time they are the product of a certain aesthetic satiety in the old world, and they are inclined to tricks and oddities, to everything strange and outlandish. If *Mystery-Bouffe* is staged with all kinds of eccentricities, then whilst its content will be repugnant to the old world, its form will remain incomprehensible to the new. But its text can be understood by anyone; it goes straight to the heart of the worker, the Red soldier, the typical impoverished peasant. It speaks for itself. It tells of the happy symbolic voyage of the working class, gradually freeing itself from its parasites after the revolutionary flood, and travelling via hell and paradise to the promised land which turns out to be our own sinful world, only cleansed by the flood of revolution and peopled by all the 'comrade things' waiting impatiently for their brother, working man. And all this is written in witty, pungent, ringing language, so that at every step of the way you meet expressions which could easily pass into everyday speech.

From my heart I wish success to this young, almost infant, yet so sincere, boisterous, exultant, unquestionably democratic and revolutionary play. From my heart I hope that the auditorium of the Theatre of Musical Drama is filled as full as possible with our true public, our worker, soldier and peasant public.

If I am a little apprehensive over the virtuosity of the Futurists, I still feel that the lively, resounding torrent of Mayakovsky's poetry will sweep away any over-modern rubbish, which is just as harmful as ancient rubbish, and will make its due mark on the public.

In any case I will not fail to go along to the performance on the evening of the anniversary day and take my friends with me. Perhaps the child will turn out deformed, but it will still be dear to us, because it is born of that same Revolution which we all regard as our own great mother.

A V LUNACHARSKY
Petrogradskaya pravda, November 1918
translated by Edward Braun

The Dawn

We have been accused today of distorting Verhaeren's amazing work. My reply is: no, Comrade Bebutov and I did not go far enough in our revision, the reason being that there was not enough time. We are too busy to spend one or two years on a single play; on our clock the second hand is all important. We can't afford to spend two or three years concocting a play which after all that time will be no more than run-of-the-mill popular propaganda. I have no doubt that at the rate we are working we are bound to go on making mistakes, but we shall make sure that we don't make the mistake of losing touch with contemporary reality as we build our theatre. We are right to invite the Cubists to work with us, because we need settings which resemble those we shall be performing against tomorrow. The modern theatre wants to move out into the open air. We want our setting to be an iron pipe or the open sea or something constructed by the new man. I don't intend to engage in an appraisal of such settings; suffice to say that for us they have the advantage of getting us out of the old theatre.

Today it has been suggested that *The Dawn* be taken away from us and given to another theatre. Long live the new RSFSR Theatre which forces theatres to stage plays other than Lecocq's *Madame Angot* and trash by Rostand. We shall be only too pleased to surrender *The Dawn* to the Moscow Art Theatre, but let them re-examine their own repertoire. If they agree to revise it and accept our play, we shall find others; we shall employ more and more Cubists and Suprematists and do away completely with the barrier of the footlights.

Perhaps we'll erect a trapeze and put our acrobats to work on it, to make their bodies express the very essence of our revolutionary theatre and remind us that we are enjoying the the struggle we are engaged in.

I agree – maybe meetings and political harangues are no use, but I am delighted that we have got *our* spectator who says to us: this is *our* theatre. I don't think there is much likelihood of the Red Army taking its banners along to *Uncle Vanya* when it came to productions which it looks on as its own. More than anyone, the Moscow Art Theatre is to blame for the passivity of the spectator whom it held in thrall for so long; at one time he was not even allowed to applaud when a surge of enthusiasm demanded applause. A theatrical performance should be a joyous event which rouses the public's emotions.

from Edward Braun,
Meyerhold on Theatre London 1969

Meyerhold
The Actor and
Biomechanics

'In the past the actor has always conformed with the society for which his art was intended. In future the actor must go even further in relating his technique to the industrial situation. For he will be working in a society where labour is no longer regarded as a curse but as a joyful, vital necessity. In these conditions of ideal labour art clearly requires a new foundation . . .

'In art our constant concern is the organisation of raw material. Constructivism has forced the artist to become both artist and engineer. Art should be based on scientific principles; the entire creative act should be a conscious process. The art of the actor consists in organising his material: that is, in his capacity to utilise correctly his body's means of expression.

'The actor embodies in himself both the organiser and that which is organised (ie the artist and his material). The formula for acting may be expressed as follows: $N = A_1 + A_2$ (where N = the actor; A_1 = the artist who conceives the idea and issues the instructions necessary for its execution; A_2 = the executant who executes the conception of A_1).

'The actor must train his material (the body), so that it is capable of executing instantaneously those tasks which are dictated externally (by the actor, the director) . . .

'Since the art of the actor is the art of plastic forms in space, he must study the mechanics of his body. This is essential because any manifestation of a force (including the living organism) is subject to constant laws of mechanics (and obviously the creation by the actor of plastic forms in the space of the stage is a manifestation of the force of the human organism) . . .

'All psychological states are determined by specific physiological processes. By correctly resolving the nature of his state physically, the actor reaches the point where he experiences the *excitation* which communicates itself to the spectator and induces him to share in the actor's performance: what we used to call "gripping" the spectator. It is this excitation which is the very essence of the actor's art. From a sequence of physical positions and situations there arise "points of excitation" which are informed with some particular emotion. Throughout this process of "rousing the emotions" the actor observes a rigid framework of physical prerequisites.'

The Magnanimous Cuckold

After the closure of the Theatre RSFSR No 1 we were left without a theatre and began to work on the problem of productions without a stage.

This was strongly reflected in the nature of the production on which we were engaged at the time. We never did have much money, and at that time we had none at all. The entire production of *The Magnanimous Cuckold* cost 200 roubles at the present rate. We were forced to put it on at the Nezlobin Theatre, where the stage was cluttered up with their gold-painted sets and hung from top to bottom with canvas flats. For us, clearing all that trash off the stage was fun, but at the same time exhausting work; naturally, the Nezlobin stage-crew was conspicuous by its absence and our entire company had to cope with the Herculean task during a break in the final rehearsals.

The production was intended to furnish the basis for a new style of acting and a new kind of setting which broke away from the conventional framing of the acting area with wings and a proscenium arch. The aim was to lay every line of the setting completely bare, and the device was pursued to the limit of schematisation. We succeeded in implementing this principle totally.

At the same time, the success of this production signified the success of the new theatrical philosophy on which it was based; now there is no doubt that the entire 'Left Theatre' not only dates from this production but to this day bears traces of its influence.

The fact that the stylistic extremes displayed by this production – although they frightened a section of critical opinion – were greeted *with delight* by the widest possible audience, proved that an urgent desire for just such a theatrical style was felt by this new audience, which regarded the theatre as one of the many *cultural* conquests of the Revolution. With this production we hoped to lay the basis for a new form of theatrical presentation with no need for illusionistic settings or complicated props, making do with the simplest objects which came to hand and transforming a spectacle performed by specialists into an improvised performance which could be put on by workers in their leisure time.

The subsequent development of our work has shown that the declared aim of this production was essential and that the whole course of modern stagecraft is leading to this end as inevitably as the advance of modern society in general.

from Edward Braun,
Meyerhold on Theatre, London 1969

Pudovkin
Mother 1926

Film + October
Lutz Becker

Film had come to Russia in May 1896 with the cameramen of the Lumière Company. First of all the country was just an interesting film subject for foreigners; then it became an important market in itself. Pathé and Gaumont followed. The first solely Russian film production started only in 1908 with the enterprises of Drankov, Chanshonkov and Yermoliev, but the foreign companies remained dominant until the First World War. Tsarist censorship was carried out by the police: representation of hard work, of historical assassinations, and any mention of the French Revolution were forbidden. Because foreign competition was cut off, the War stimulated the home market and home production. Private enterprises began to flourish. In February 1917 Kerensky came to power and censorship was abolished for a period, but the structure of the film industry remained untouched. This early part of Russian film history is less known and explored, less significant in the light of the great changes brought about by the October Revolution, although it must be said that the art of film was already well developed.

The films of this period were highly theatrical but quite a number of them were of great artistry. In this theatrical genre a generation of film makers was trained and, after the Revolution, it contributed to the new Soviet Cinema. The most prominent of these were Yakow Protasanov, Alexander Sanin and Vladimir Gardin. After the Soviet victory most of the original film people were swept away or went into exile. A new generation of young film enthusiasts entered on the scene; they were filled with the excitement of the times, and with enthusiasm for the idea and love of 'the people'. Because the defeated capitalists had destroyed or moved away the film equipment, films could only be made under the greatest difficulties. There were only a few cameras left and hardly any film stock. This educated a generation that could improvise, that was responsible towards the apparatus as well as towards the chosen subject. A new type of cameraman was born at the war front, fighting with the Red Army, or travelling with the agit-trains and agit-ships into the remotest parts of the Union. Great involvement with the people's problems, great hopes, heated argument, learning and teaching inspired by Lenin's Revolution, brought into these films a realism and integrity of a hitherto unknown intensity. Under these extraordinary circumstances, reflecting and recording, cameramen found extraordinary images. The dimension discovered was that of revolutionary aims, of political and personal hopes. The present was seen in the light of the future; the shadow of the past was wiped away with a new optimism.

The new Soviet government gave aid and stimulus to the struggling film people. All matters of film were administered by a subdivision of the People's Commissariat of Education under the leadership of Anatoli Lunacharsky. Thanks to the personal efforts and intellectual scope of Lunarcharsky, film of this time developed freely in every direction.

However, it was only after Lenin's Decree on the Nationalisation of the Film Industry on 27 August 1919 that film production was established on a fully co-ordinated basis and which was fully focused on topical aims. Lenin is reported to have said: 'The art of film is for us the most important of all arts.' He saw film serving cultural and educational aims, according to the maxims of the Communist Party.

1 film chronicle (newsreel and documentary)
2 film lecture (popular, scientific and educational)
3 feature film (artistically staged expression of ideas)

The winter of famine, 1919–20, stopped nearly all film work; the pressures of civil war, foreign intervention and blockades were overpowering. This forced the government to enter the New Economical Policy (NEP) which meant a temporary return to a semi-capitalist system. In 1922 a state-owned film company was founded, GOSKINO, from 1924 onwards called SOVKINO. Subsidiary companies were: GOSKINO, MESHRABPOM-RUSS, GOSVOYENKINO, PROLETKINO, LENINGRADKINO, KULTKINO. The studios in the non-Russian Soviet republics were subsidiaries of their local educational commissariats, as was Wufku in the Ukraine. Film scripts and films were censored by a film committee, 'Glavrepertkom' (Committee for the control of repertoire). In 1928 the first of the Five Year Plans came into action. In 1930 the firm SOVKINO was dissolved and a new organisation established, SOIUSKINO which, although it was under economic direction from the Ministry of Finance, received its ideological guidance from the single educational commissariats of the Soviet Republics. With these changes in the pattern of the industry and the change of emphasis on the responsibility and social function of film makers, the art of film was developing rapidly in the speed of the Revolution. Together with historically and economically favourable situations, a climate arose that stimulated a great creativity in all fields of film. The feedback between the arts, the teaming-up of talented people from all cultural spheres, generated in addition a dynamic co-operation, lively competition, and mutual revolutionary aims gave these people the framework of a purposeful discipline.

Dziga Vertov (pseudonym of Denis Kaufman, 1896–1954) was to become the first important Soviet film maker and theoretician. He started in 1917 as compiler and editor of the first Soviet newsreel, *Kino-Nedelya* – 42 issues, which obtained pictures from the cameramen who were at the front and with the agit-trains. Then he collaborated on the compilation film *History of the Civil War*. Between 1922 and 1925 he directed and edited the monthly reel *Kino-Pravda* (*Film Truth*) – 23 issues. These reels were to become not only the chronicle of the years but also the artistic reflection which captured the events in addition to the texture, the feeling, the dynamism of a society in transformation. The use of close-ups, the

rhythm in his editing style, were subjective expression and agitation. The titles of the reels, designed by Rodchenko, were well integrated and placed information and slogans contra-punctual to the flow of the images. In his approach he had at first been influenced by the futurists, but he developed his theories on the Constructivist basis. He discovered a new humanity, the man as master of the machine: the scientifically oriented man; the researcher; the active and critical cameraman; the camera-eye. In 1923 he said in a manifesto printed in the magazine *LEF*:

I am an eye. I am a mechanical eye. I, the machine, show you a world the way only I can see it. I free myself for today and forever from human immobility. I am in constant movement. I approach and pull away from objects. I creep under them. I move alongside a running horse's mouth. I cut into a crowd in full speed. I run in front of running soldiers. I turn over on my back. I soar with an aeroplane. I fall and rise with the falling and rising bodies. This is I, the machine, manoeuvring in the chaotic movements, recording one movement after another in the most complex combinations. Freed from the obligation of shooting 16 to 17 frames per second, freed from the boundaries of time and space, I co-ordinate any and all points of the universe, wherever I want them to be. My way leads towards the creation of a fresh perception of the world. Thus I explain in a new way the world unknown to you.

With his faithful Kinoki team (Zh Svilova, I Kopalin, B Kudinov, P Sotov, M Bushin, Michael Kaufman), he made four short films, *Kino-Glas* (*Film Eye*), in which he defined his style further, strengthened the editing-principle, developed the flashback and the shifting of the time element. In this manner he stepped away from the merely representative to the construction of life, the artistic method fused with the scientific. The clash of the old and the new in everyday life, he transformed into a filmic conflict that opened the eye for the vision of the future. In 1926 he made two films, *Forward Soviet* and *One sixth of the Earth*, both political documentary films. These two films had a great influence on Soviet documentary film making, for instance *Turksib* by Victor Turin (1929). His montage principle was taken over by Esfir Shub, who applied it to compilation film. *The Man With the Movie Camera* (1929) is perhaps the purest of the kino-glas films. It is like an illustration of a Vertov manifesto. The cameraman and the camera are the subject of the film. When sound appeared, Vertov also related his principles to the sound material which he handled in free montage. Similar to the Italian futurist, Pratella (1912), he aimed towards a collage of noises of all kinds. But while the futurists had seen it as an end in itself, Vertov gave it a dramatic functional purpose. His films *Donbas Symphony* (1931) and *Three Songs of Lenin* (1934) were truly sound films of great strength. According to the Leninist Film Proportion, his films had engineered an important role for the documentary film, in the industry as well as in distribution. He expanded cinema to a degree which is not yet properly evaluated.

Esfir Shub (1894–1959) became Vertov's fellow fighter for Lenin's idea of proportion. She started as an editor of foreign language title versions in 1922. She assisted Sergei Eisenstein in the editing of *Strike* and under Vertov's influence she started working on documentary films. Her great revolutionary intention was to use old stock footage for compilation films: according to the principle of ideological

montage. In this way she opened up the possibilities for the compilation film as an art in itself. Thanks to her laborious efforts, many rolls of films from the early days of the Revolution have been preserved. Her main films are: *The End of the Romanov Dynasty* (1926), *The Great Road* (1927), *The Russia of Nikolai II and Leo Tolstoi* (1928) and *Today* (1930).

Lev Kuleshov (1899–1970) became the great teacher of the new film generation. Though of the same age as Vertov and Pudovkin, his particular gift for experimentation in bridging theatre and film, made him their master. Kuleshov had originally been a painter and a theatre-set designer. The theatre director, Yevgeni Bauer, influenced him greatly, which is apparent from an article he wrote in 1917. 'The artist of the cinema paints with objects, walls and lights . . . It is almost unimportant what is in the shot. What is really important is to dispose of these objects and re-combine them for the purpose of their final single plane.' Meyerhold and his theory of Biomechanics influenced Kuleshov's work with actors. Movement was the basis of his acting theory; not psychology but physical reality, not meditation but analysis. In 1920 Kuleshov became a drama teacher at the Moscow Film Institute. In the same year he made a film with his class: *At the Red Front*. With this film and further systematic research, he developed the basic principles of montage: that it is not the content of the single shot which is important, but the way one shot is cut together with the next; that one sequence alone cannot give sufficient definition – it has to be cut together with the other sequences that make up the film. Together with his theories on acting, his principle of montage formed a very sophisticated method of feature film making. He created the specifically trained film actor, as opposed to the theatre actor. The results were a highly cinematic action comparable to the intensity of the German expressionists, an objective extrapolation of psychological matter, the creation of the filmic archetype. In 1923 he made *The Strange Adventures of Mr West in the Land of the Bolsheviks* and in 1925 *Deathray*. His masterpiece was *By the Law* (1926), scripted together with Victor Shklovsky. The number of films produced by Kuleshov remained small. He was a dedicated teacher of many generations of film makers.

Sergei M Eisenstein (1898–1948) never had lessons with Kuleshov, but his work was rooted in the master's innovations. Eisenstein was born in Riga and studied at the Petersburg Institute of Civil Engineering. When he was demobilised in 1920, after two years in the fortification unit of the Red Army, he joined the Proletkult Theatre. Here he came under the influence of Meyerhold's approach to theatre, assisted at Foregger's Theatre, and took lessons with Meyerhold. The theatre as an 'instrument for social proclamations' and as a place of popular entertainment, the actor as an artist, all became the basis for Eisenstein's first Theory of the *Montage of Attractions*, which was already closely related to his future film work. This theory was published in 1923 in the same issue of *LEF* as that in which Vertov published his manifesto to *Kinoks Revolution*.

> The attraction (in our diagnosis of the theatre) is every aggressive moment in it, ie every element of it that brings to light in the spectator those senses or that psychology that influence his experience – every element that can be verified and mathematically calculated to produce certain emotional shocks in a proper order within the totality – the only means by which it is possible to make the final ideological conclusion perceptible. The way to knowledge – 'through the living play of the passions' – applies specially to the theatre (perceptually).

> Approached genuinely, this basically determines the possible principles of construction as 'an action construction' (of the whole production). Instead of a static 'reflection' of an event with all possibilities for activity within the limits of the event's logical action, we advance to a new plane – free montage of arbitrarily selected, independent (within the given composition and the subject links that hold the influencing actions together) attractions – all from the stand of establishing certain final thematic effects – this is montage of attractions.

The theatre is confronted with the problem of transforming its 'illusory pictures' and its 'presentations' into a montage of 'real matters' while at the same time weaving into the montage full 'pieces of representation' tied to the plot development of the subject, but now not as self-enforced and all-determining, but as consciously contributing to the whole production and selected for their pure strength as active attractions.

First of all Eisenstein liberated theatre from the stage and went with actors to the Winter Palace to stage the Revolution; then he went to the gasworks to perform to the workers in their own environment. With members of the Proletkult, including Grigori Alexandrov, he scripted and made the film *Strike* in 1924. This film contained many elements of the Proletkult: the types, the fast action. Its cameraman was Eduard Tissé (1897–1961) who had started film work with Vertov's *Kino-Nedelya* and remained from then on with Eisenstein. The second film was made in 1925: *Battleship Potemkin*. It was originally intended as part of a long film marking the twentieth anniversary of the abortive revolution of 1905, but Eisenstein expanded one sequence, the mutiny in Odessa, and made it the epitome of the whole revolution. This film became the greatest example of the montage theory Eisenstein had developed out of his theatrical theory, and Vertov's and Kuleshov's findings, which he combined with his own film experiences. The film found its famous climax in the steps sequence, which he shot with several cameras. The dynamic and dramatic use of the close-up and long-shot, the clash of contrasts and rhythms that Vertov had demanded from documentary film, were used here for the first time in a feature film.

1927 saw a flurry of activity among Soviet film makers to produce films for the tenth anniversary of the Revolution. Eisenstein had already started work on his next production, *The Old and the New*, which he interpreted in order to make *October* (1927). Within a few months, this production was disrupted through Trotsky's departure, and had to be re-edited. Though this film did not have the great unity of his previous works, it created the Revolution with authenticity and dramatic power. The associative and ideological montage formed sequences of complex thoughts, not just stories. This made Eisenstein's first creative period. In the years after, he established and expanded his theories in writing and became a teacher at the Moscow Film Institute. He continued to speak in his writings with the same forceful language of revolution he had used in his films. He was, and is, a spiritual leader for many film makers because he combined great creativity with a scientific, analytical mind.

Vsevolod Pudovkin (1893–1953) started off as an actor, assisted Sardin for two years, and went to Kuleshov's workshop in Moscow. Only here he became conscious of the possibilities of film, and even though he approached film acting in a different way, his films owe much to Kuleshov. His first film was *Chess Fever* (1925), which shows this influence clearly. In 1926, he started working on the film *Mechanics of the Brain* which he interrupted to make *Mother*, using Maxim Gorky's novel and documents of the 1905 uprising. In its impact the film is comparable with *Battleship Potemkin*, also in the quality of imagination, political seriousness and humanity. Pudovkin's emphasis lies on the individual hero, based on the reality of a literal subject. The formal aim was not in the direction of the masses and the clash of attractions, but in the shots which were held for a long time, allowing an internal rhythm to develop. This permitted the actors Vera Barnovskaia and Nicolai Batalov to bring into the film the whole weight of their personalities. Thus Pudovkin was able to utilise the realistic qualities which Constantin Stanislavsky had instilled in his actors, and became more and more in opposition with Kuleshov and Eisenstein.

Pudovkin combined the work with psychological acting and the latest montage principles. His film had a well-balanced rhythmical basis, and the montage of close-ups was well used to transmit the physical reality. Editing rhythm was only used to evoke emotion and sympathy. Elliptic montage patterns linked individual with objective material and introduced visual leitmotifs. Pudovkin's early experience with the chamber-play allowed him now to use the set and lighting to make psychological situations visible, just as German expressionism was doing at the same time. In 1928 he wrote his book *Film Technique and Film Acting* in which he laid down his theories on the relationship between montage and acting and film continuity. With these theories he was closer to social realism than were any other of his contemporaries, with the exception of Alexander Dovshenko. In 1927 he made *The End of St Petersburg*. Its theme as well as the location, the Winter Palace, coincided with Eisenstein's *October*. While Eisenstein's film is the embodiment of the Revolution, Pudovkin's film shows the same event as a slow mental process, the process of self-discovery of specific figures. His next film *Storm Over Asia*, 1928, displayed similar lyric and epic qualities, again representing the process of slow self-liberation towards definite political conclusions.

Alexander P Dovshenko (1894–1956) had been a teacher and painter, and in 1926 he entered Vufku, the Ukranian Film Company, as a script writer. Through his work specific regional qualities entered film. Most of his films were made in the Ukraine later on, and this influenced his film work and its basic simplicity. Based on the ancient art of story-telling, his films gained a wonderful poetical structure and depth. His first film was *Vassia the Reformer* (1926), followed by *Svenigora* (1928). The latter was a highly personal statement, a poem full of memories and allegories and an endless wealth in pictorial ideas. In *Arsenal* (1929) he portrayed the Ukrainian Revolution. Of this he said: 'Gigantic events have forced me to compress my material under the pressure of many atmospheres. This can be done if one uses poetic language, which seems to be my speciality.' *Earth*, produced in 1930, is the most harmonious film he made. The slow rhythm, the epic dramaturgy, have balanced up the faster moments of montage and have defined Allegory to Symbol. The contrast between the shots is more a contrast of texture, of life and death, than a clash of physical actions. All his films convey a great feeling for landscape, and the rhythm of nature, the rhythm of the seasons. The social idea is bound up with the question of fate; the political emotion is closely linked with an active practical attitude. Certainly he was indebted to the innovations contributed to film editing by his colleagues, but his personality did not allow for the formation of theories; for him everything was constantly changing. In a sense his films were technically quite traditional, but in their content and perspective, new and moving.

Gregory Kosintzev (born 1905) and **Leonid Trauberg** (born 1902) came from the theatre. Inspired by the Proletkult and the Meyerhold Theatre, also by American slapstick comedy, in 1921 they published their *Manifesto of the Eccentric Actor*, a piece of revolutionary prose praising the forces of change and the dynamic positivism in art:

The key to the events.

1 Yesterday: a comfortable office. Bold forehead. They meditated, came to decisions racked their brains. Today: Signal! To the machines! Driving belts, chains, wheels, hands, legs, electricity. The rhythm of productivity. Yesterday: museums, temples, libraries. Today: factories, enterprises, building sites.

2 Yesterday: the culture of Europe. Today: the technology of America, industrialisation, production under the Stars and Stripes. Oh, Americanisation! Oh, undertaker!

3 Yesterday: saloons, reverences, baronets. Today: the exclamations of the newspaper boys, scandals, police truncheons, noise, screaming, scraping, haste – rhythms of today.

On this basis they gathered friends, including Sergei Yutkevitch (born 1905). In 1922 in St Petersburg, they opened the *Factory of the Eccentric Actor* (FEKS), an acting workshop. In 1924, they made together their first film *The Adventures of an October Child*, and in 1926 *The Devil's Wheel*. These films were full of fantasy and had a great sense of the absurd, still closely related to American film burlesque. Obviously under the influence of Kuleshov, they improved their method and introduced some artistic restraint into their work. *The Greatcoat* (1926), following a screen adaptation of Gogol's theme, came very close to German expressionism. The figures were drawn in a grotesque way, a tension between the innocent and the haunted was established through a very careful use of lighting and design. This poetic use of film language carried with it a breath of nostalgia, pity for lost hopes and enthusiasm towards new hopes. The film rhythm was even; feelings were mainly created within the shot. Two films with revolutionary themes were made: in 1927, *SWD The Club of the Great Deed* and in 1929, *New Babylon*.

Yakov Protazanov (1881–1945) came from theatre and started a very successful career as film director during the Tsarist period. After a few years in French and German exile, he returned to the Soviet Union and started a new career. Under the influence of Meyerhold and German Expressionism he made the film *Aelita* (1924) which was an adaptation of a novel by Alexei Tolstoi. 1925 brought *The Tailor of Torshok* and 1927 *The Fortyfirst*. His productions, based on traditional principles, were a constantly reassuring factor, the quality was often admired, and had some influence in the development of Soviet cinema and its continuity. His sense for the psychology of his characters was especially remarkable.

Abram Room (born 1894) is, next to Sanin, Olga Preobrazhenskaya and Yuri Sheliabushky, the dominant film director of the naturalist school. He had started as an actor in amateur theatricals and later worked on the Meyerhold stage. In 1926 he made his first film *The Death Ray* and in 1927 he made *Bed and Sofa*, one of the most controversial films of the period, dealing, with great sociological sense, with the problem of free love. The script was by Victor Shklovsky. With this film he captured with simplicity some of the problems of the new post-revolutionary generation. In 1930 he made *The Ghost That Never Returned*, where he recreated the revolutionary situation in a South American country. His naturalism, together with the realistic tendencies evident in the work of other film makers of the period, formed the basis for the coming social realism.

The excitement of this early period that lasted from 1917 until the early 1930s, the fire of the battle of ideas, the ardour of the revolutionary work, has impregnated all the artistic results. Through an act of self-liberation a nation stepped within a few years from a byzantine mediaeval structured society, towards the society of the future. And this happened in spite of attacks from inside and outside enemies. The great hopes that had arisen in those days were of such passion which found expression in all the arts and has not lost its strength and topicality. The constructivists were the first to recognise the necessity for a new form, for a new content. On film they demanded: 'The art of the film has to become an effective expression and weapon of the new society' (Esfir Shub).

The aesthetic solutions were bound on to the newly gained sense of reality and on to social-political functions. Film had recorded face and structure of the people and of the revolutionary events, it gave interpretations, it made the new ideas and the changes they had provoked understood to the masses, it contributed to the creation of a new self-understanding of the liberated society. Film got a social function and a status equal to the other arts and communication media. Out of this new strength the Soviet film gained great masterworks. Not alone economical and political factors but most exceptional historical circumstances allowed great talents to develop genius.

Eisenstein
Strike 1924

Vesnin
Mock-up house for *The General Line* 1927

Protazonov
Aelita 1924

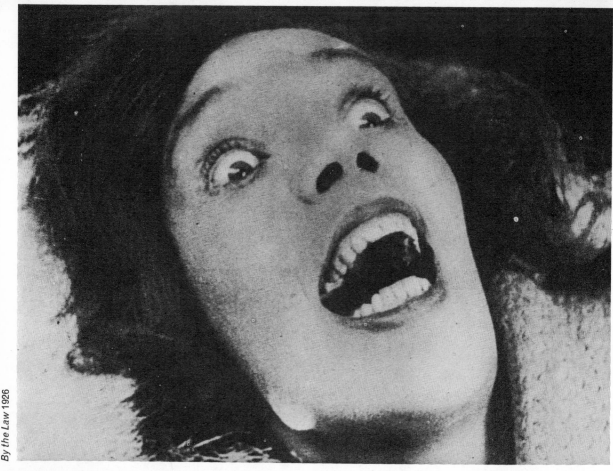

Vertov
The man with the movie camera 1929

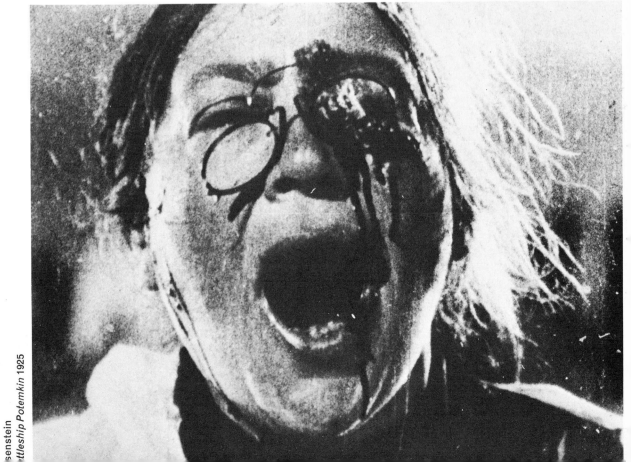

senstein
ttleship Potemkin 1925

Dovshenko
Arsenal 1929

Vertov
WE

WE call ourselves Kinoki – to distinguish
ourselves from the 'cinematographists' – this
horde of rag-pickers which makes good
business out of its old rags.

WE see no connection between the
cold-blooded and penny-pinching profiteers
and true and honest filmwork.
The psychological Russian-German
filmdrama, burdened with daydreams and
childhood memories, we consider to be
nonsense.
Kinok thanks the American adventure film, the
film with apparent dynamism, the creations of
the American Pinkerton film business, and the
rapid change of imagery and the close-up.
They are used quite well there but not according
to an order, not based on the precise study of
movement. A higher level of the psychological
drama – but without basis. Cliché. Imitation of
an imitation.

WE declare: the old films, the romantic ones,
the theatrical ones and others of this kind – are
leprous.
– don't go too near them!
– turn your eyes from them!
– they are deadly!
– danger of infection!

WE maintain: the future of the art of film lies in
the disregard of these fabrications.
The death of 'cinematography' is necessary for
the survival of film art.

WE appeal to hasten its death.

WE protest against the mixture of the arts
which many call 'synthesis'.
The mixture of bad colours, even the mixture of
the purest colours of the spectrum results not
in white – but in dirt.
Synthesis is possible at the peak of
accomplishment in each art-form and not
before.

WE want to free film from all elements that
intrude: Music, Literature and Theatre.

WE search for its own unpurloined rhythm that
will not have been stolen from somewhere
else, we find it in the movement of objects.

WE demand:

– *away*
from the sweet hugs of Romance, from the poisonous haze of the psychological novel, from the claws of amateur theatre, from music.

– *away*
into the pure field of the film, into the width of four dimensions (three plus time) in the search for its own material, its own measure, its own rhythm. The 'psychological' hinders man from being precise like a stopwatch, hinders him in his desire to unite closely with the machine.

WE see no reason for directing most of our attention on to today's man while we study movement.

One has to be ashamed in front of machines at man's inability to behave; what else can we do when the immaculate manners of the machines excite us more than the brainless haste or the lousy inactivity of unconcerned people? The gaiety of dancing saws in the saw-mill is more comprehensible to us, and closer to us, than human caperings.

WE leave (from time to time) the object man out of our shots, because it is incapable of controlling its movements.

Our way: from the 'master of creation' who got stuck in his work, over to the poetry of the machine towards the perfect, electrical man.

WE discover the souls of the machines, we are in love with the worker at his bench, we are in love with the farmer on his tractor, the engineer on his locomotive.

WE bring creative joy into every mechanical activity.

WE make peace between man and machine.

WE educate the new man.

The new man, freed of his clumsiness and incompetence, in the possession of the precise and light movements of the machine will be a wonderful subject for the film camera.

WE discover in ourselves an understanding for the rhythm of the machines, an enthusiasm for man's work, for chemical processes.

WE praise the earthquake.

WE compose film-poems about factory chimneys, and power stations.

WE are inspired by the orbit of comets and meteors.

WE dazzle the stars with our projectors. Everybody who loves his art, searches for the basic principle of its technique.

The failing nerves of cinematography need the strong system of regular processes.

Film length, speed, the nature of movement and its precise position in relation to the co-ordinate-axis of the image, and the co-ordinate-axis of the earth too (three dimensions plus the fourth, being time), have to be studied by every film-maker.

Necessity, precision and speed – three requirements of every movement which is worthy of photography and projection.

What we demand of the editing: to discover the geometrical extract of each shot.

Filmwork is the art of organising the necessary movements of objects in space, whereby the rhythmical and artistic result is adjusted towards the properties of the material and the internal rhythm of each object.

Material-artistic elements of the movement are the intervals (the transitions from one movement to the other), but not the movements themselves. They (the intervals) carry the action towards its kinetic conclusion.

The organisation of movement is the organisation of its elements, that is to say the intervals within a phrase.
Each phrase includes rise, climax, fall of a movement (in proportion to its importance).
A work is constructed out of phrases, like a a phrase is built up out of the intervals of a movement.

Once having found an idea or pattern for a
film-poem, the Kinok should be able to note
it down precisely, in order to bring his plan
under the best possible circumstances alive
on the screen.
The complete scenario naturally cannot
replace such original notes, like a libretto
could never replace a pantomime, or like the
literary commentaries to the works of Skriabin
give no notion of his music.
To present dynamic study on paper one needs
to represent the movement graphically.

WE are in search of the Kinogram.

WE fall, we rise with the rhythm of movement,
slowed down or speeded up, away from us,
beside us, towards us, in a circle, straight, in
an ellipse, to the right and to the left, with the
signs plus and minus; the movements distort,
stretch, part from each other, minimise or
multiply, they fly silent through space.

Film is also the art of inventing movement of
objects in space to meet the demands of
science; it realises the dreams of the inventor
or the scientist, the artist, the engineer or
carpenter. The film realises the possibilities
of life. Drawings in motion. Sketches in motion.
Designs of future things. The theory of
relativity on the screen.

WE welcome the regular phantasy of the
movements. Borne by the wings of the
hypothesis our propellor-eyes fly into the
future.

WE believe that the moment is nearing in
which we will be able to throw hurricanes of
movement into space, ruled only by our method.

Long live dynamic geometry, the race of points
and lines, planes and volumes. Long live the
poetry of ever-turning machines, the poetry
of levers, of wheels and wings of steel, the
lonely shriek of movements, the blinding
flash of glowing streams.

First printed in Kinophot No 1 1922
Translated (from German) by Lutz Becker

Lenin
Decree

On the transfer of the Photographic and
Cinematographic Trade and Industry to The
Peoples Commissariat of Education.

1 The entire photographic and cinematographic
  trade and industry, their organisation as well
  as the supply and distribution of technical
  means and materials appertaining to them,
  throughout the territory of the RSFSR, shall
  be placed within the province of the People's
  Commissariat of Education.

2 To this end the People's Commissariat of
  Education is herewith empowered:
a to nationalise, by agreement with the Supreme
  Council of National Economy, particular photo
  and cinema enterprises, as well as the entire
  photo and cinema industry;
b to requisition enterprises as well as photo
  and cinema goods, materials and equipment;
c to fix stable and maximum prices for photo and
  cinema raw materials and manufactured
  products;
d to exercise supervision and control over the
  photo and cinema trade and industry, and
e to regulate the entire photo and cinema trade
  and industry by issuing decisions which shall
  be binding on enterprises and private persons,
  as well as on Soviet Institutions, insofar as they
  relate to photo and cinema matters.

Chairman of the Council
of Peoples Commissars: V Ulyanov (Lenin)

Executive Officer of the
Council of People's Commissars:
Vlad Bonch-Bruyevich

Moscow, Kremlin
27 August 1919

Translation by Jay Leyda

Eisenstein
The Method of
Making Workers Films

There is one *method* for making *any* film: montage of attractions. To know what this is and why, see the book, *Cinema Today*, where, rather dishevelled and illegible, my approach to the construction of film works is described.

Our class approach introduces:
1 A *specific purpose for the work* – a socially useful emotional and psychological affect on the audience; this to be composed of a chain of suitably directed stimulants. This *socially useful affect* I call the *content of the work*.

It is thus possible, for example, to define the *content* of a production. *Do You Hear, Moscow?*: the maximum tension of aggressive reflexes in social protest. *Strike*: an accumulation of reflexes without intervals (satisfaction), that is, a focusing of reflexes on struggle (and a lifting of potential class tone).

2 A *choice of stimulants*. In two directions. In making a correct appraisal of the class inevitability of their nature, certain stimulants are capable of evoking a certain reaction (affect) only among spectators of a certain class. For a more precise affect the audience must be even more unified, if possible along professional lines: any director of 'living newspaper' performances in clubs knows how different audiences, say metal workers or textile workers, react completely differently and at different places to the same work.

Such class 'inevitability' in matters of action can be easily illustrated by the amusing failure of one attraction that was strongly affected by the circumstances of one audience: I refer to the slaughter-house sequence in *Strike*. Its concentratedly associative affect of bloodiness among certain strata of the public is well known. The Crimean censor even cut it, along with the latrine scene. (That certain sharp affects are inadmissable was indicated by an American after seeing *Strike*: he declared that this scene would surely have to be removed before the film was sent abroad.) It was the same kind of simple reason that prevented the usual

'bloody' affect of the slaughter-house sequence from shocking certain worker-audiences: among these workers the blood of oxen is first of all associated with the by-product factories near the slaughter-house! And for peasants who are accustomed to the slaughter of cattle this affect would also be cancelled out.

The other direction in the choice of stimulants appears to be the class accessibility of this or that stimulant.

Negative examples: the variety of sexual attractions that are fundamental to the majority of bourgeois works placed on the market: methods that lead one away from concrete reality, such as the sort of expressionism used in *Caligari*; or the sweet middle-class poison of Mary Pickford, the exploited and systematically trained stimulation of all middle class inclinations, even in our healthy and advanced audiences.

The bourgeois cinema is no less aware than we are of class taboos. In New York City's censorship regulations we find a list of thematic attractions undesirable for film use: 'relations between labour and capital' appears alongside 'sexual perversion', 'excessive brutality', 'physical deformity'...

The study of stimulants and their montage for a particular purpose provides us with exhaustive materials on the question of *form*. As I understand it, content is the *summary of all that is subjected to the series of shocks* to which in a particular order the audience is to be exposed. (Or more crudely: so much per cent of material to fix the attention, so much to rouse the bitterness, etc.) But this material must be organised in accordance with a principle that leads to the desired effect.

Form is the *realisation of these intentions* in a particular material, as precisely those stimulants which are able to summon this indispensable per cent are created and assembled in the concrete expression of the factual side of the work.

One should, moreover, keep in mind the 'attractions of the moment', that is, those reactions that flame forth temporarily in connection with certain courses or events of social life.

In contrast to these there are a series of 'eternal' attractions, phenomena and methods

Some of these have a class usefulness. For example, a healthy and integrated audience always reacts to an epic of class struggle.

Equal with these are the 'neutrally' affective attractions, such as death-defying stunts, *double entendres*, and the like.

To use these independently leads to *l'art pour l'art* so as to reveal their counter-revolutionary essence.

As with the attraction moments, one ought to remember that neutral or accidental attractions cannot, ideologically, be taken for granted, but should be used only as a method of exciting those unconditioned reflexes that are necessary to us not in themselves but in the training of socially useful conditioned reflexes that we wish to combine with certain objectives of our social aims.

This manifesto appeared in *KING* on 11 August 1925. Translation by Jay Leyda (in *Film Essays* by S Eisenstein published 1968 by Dennis Dobson

| Третьяков | Брик | Маяковский | Родченко | Асеев |

Кушнер

Шкловский

ЧИТАЙТЕ

НОВЫЙ ЛЕФ

В. В. Маяковский

ГОСИЗДАТ

Степанова

Лавинский

Вертов

ПОДПИСЫВАЙТЕСЬ

На год
12 книг

На 6 мес.
6 книг

Эйзенштейн

TRETYAKOV   BRIK   MAYAKOVSKY   RODCHENKO   ASEYEV

READ

KUSHNER   # NOVY   SHKLOVSKY
                         # LEF

MAYAKOVSKY

STEPANOVA   LAVINSKY

State Publishing House

VERTOV   # SUBSCRIBE   EISENSTEIN

Yearly   6 monthly
12   6

KIRSANOV   NEZNAMOV   ZHEMCHUZHNY   PASTERNAK   PERTSOV

Novy Lef
1927-28

Guide

Exhibits not credited to other
sources have been supplied by the
Ministry of Culture of the USSR.

THE FIRST YEARS OF THE SOVIET UNION
a film by Lutz Becker
made from original Soviet documentary
footage, especially from the *Kino-Nedelya* and
Kino-Pravda reels (1917–25) of Dziga Vertov

Edited in the manner of the period, but for
projection on three screens so that concurrent
historical events can be shown simultaneously
and can be allowed to comment on each other.

It covers the last phase of the First World War
and the immediate post-Revolution years:
the Tsar
civil war
foreign intervention
Lenin's decrees on peace and on the
distribution of the land
the mobilisation of the civil population for its
new tasks
the creation of the Red Army

In it we see the political and artistic leaders of
the new Soviet state, the workers, the peasants
and the soldiers. It describes the new dynamic
world served by the art and design featured in
this exhibition, its problems and its aspirations.

F

AGIT-PROP
agitational propaganda, or the political,
economic and cultural education of the masses.
One of the first tasks of the new state was to
spread its principles and ideals among the
masses in whose name it was established, and
to exhort them to join in defeating counter-
Revolutionary forces and to strengthen society
by developing agriculture and industry. Many
artists (including Mayakovsky the poet) found
in this task an application of their skills
relevant to the new society and their own dreams
of being useful members of it.

POSTERS
by
LISSITZKY
RODCHENKO
MOOR
DEINEKA
KLUTSIS
MAYAKOVSKY
CHEREMNYKH
ZAILER
and others

A simulated AGIT-TRAIN of the sort that were
sent out all over the country, carrying officials,
poets, and artists, to spread Soviet ideas and
news in word and image

ADVERTISING POSTERS, mostly for films
by
V & G STENBERG
BELSKY
KUSTODIEV
PRUSAKOV
LAVINSKY
and others

original and reproduced documentation
showing design work for MASS FESTIVALS
by
ALEKSEYEVA
A & V VESNIN
PUNIN
KUSTODIEV
ALTMAN
LEBEDEV
DOBUZHINSKY
STERNBERG
ANNENKOV
and others

POPULAR SONGS on the first post-
Revolutionary years

AP

THEATRE
new ideas in design and production in the Soviet
theatre

MODELS

LAVINSKY and KhRAKOVSKY
set for *Mystery-Bouffe* (Mayakovsky) produced
by Meyerhold at the RSFSR Theatre No 1,
Moscow 1921
(Bakhrushin State Theatre Museum, Moscow)

POPOVA
set for *The Magnanimous Cuckold*
(Crommelynck) produced by Meyerhold at the
Actor's Theatre, Moscow 1922
(reconstruction by the Bristol University Drama
Department; scale 1:4)

STEPANOVA
set for *Tarelkin's Death* (Sukhovo-Kobylin)
produced by Meyerhold at the Actor's Theatre,
Moscow 1922
(reconstruction by Philip Wood; scale 1:4)

ALEXANDER VESNIN
set for *The Man who was Thursday* (after
Chesterton), produced by Tairov at the
Kamerny Theatre, Moscow 1923
(reconstruction by Ariane Lewis; scale 1:10)

SHLEPYANOV
set for *The Warrant* (Erdman) produced by
Meyerhold at the Meyerhold Theatre,
Moscow 1925
(Bakhrushin State Theatre Museum, Moscow)

LISSITZKY
set for *I Want a Child* (Tretyakov) commissioned
by Meyerhold for production at the Meyerhold
Theatre, Moscow, and worked on during 1926–9,
but never realised
(reconstruction by Philip Wood; scale 1:20)

VLADIMIR and GIORGY STENBERG
set for *The Hairy Ape* (O'Neill) produced by
Tairov at the Kamerny Theatre, Moscow 1929
(Bakhrushin State Theatre, Museum, Moscow)

SHTOFFER
set for *A Flying Start* (Stavsky and
Pavlutchenko) produced by Okhlopkov at the
Theatre of the Revolution, Moscow 1932
(Bakhrushin State Theatre Museum, Moscow)

DESIGNS for sets and costumes
by
EXTER
EISENSTEIN
RODCHENKO
V & G STENBERG
YAKULOV
LENTULOV
A VESNIN
SIMOV
and others

PHOTOGRAPHS of productions
by
TAIROV
MEYERHOLD
EISENSTEIN
OKhLOPKOV
and others

PHOTOMONTAGE
by Lutz Becker
illustrating contemporary political and social life
in the Soviet Union through documentary
material of the period, notably from the work of
Lissitzky and Rodchenko, drawing on the
magazines *Lef* and *Novy Lef* (1923–5 and 1927–8;
edited by Mayakovsky)

T

ARCHITECTURE
progressive architectural design of the 1920s,
realised and projected

MODELS

TATLIN
project for the Monument to the Third
International, 1919–20, to rise to a height of over
1,200 feet and to house assembly halls,
government offices and a communications
centre in variously rotating structures supported
within the steel skeleton, and intended (it is said)
to be erected in Petrograd over the river Neva
(reconstruction by Christopher Cross, Jeremy
Dixon, Sven, Rindl, Peter Watson and
Christopher Woodward; scale 1 : 50)
shown on the sculpture court

ALEXANDER VESNIN
project for the *Leningrad Pravda* offices, 1923–4
(reconstruction by Michael Gold and Edward
Jones; scale 1 : 15)

LEONIDOV
project for the Lenin Institute, 1927
a spherical assembly hall and a vertical library
(book stack), with adjacent study rooms etc,
to be built near Moscow and linked to the city by
means of an overhead road and railway
(reconstruction by Stuart Wrede and Michael
Carapetian; scale 1 : 250)

GINSBURG
project for flats in a communal housing unit,
1928
(reconstruction by Roger Foster; scale 1 : 20)

MELNIKOV
the Rusakov Club, Moscow 1927–9
(reconstruction by Mark Sewell of Thurloe
Models Ltd; scale 1 : 50)

MELNIKOV
the architect's own house, Moscow 1929
(reconstruction by Mark Sewell of Thurloe
Models Ltd; scale 1 : 10)

PHOTOGRAPHS
and other documentation to
show
TOWN PLANNING
and the development of old
towns
by
LEONIDOV
LAVROV
A SHVIDKOVSKY
teams from OSA, ARU, etc
(architectural associations)
FRIEDMAN
GINSBURG
SHESTAKOV
LADOVSKY
and others

NEW TYPES OF DWELLINGS AND PUBLIC BUILDINGS
by
GOLOSOV
BARKHIN
A V & L VESNIN
MILINIS
GINSBURG
LAVROV
BARSHCH
SERAFIMOV
SHCHUSEV
LISSITZKY
MELNIKOV
SHUKHOV
FOMIN
LADOVSKY
VAKhTANGOV
SHCHUKO
GELFREICH
architectural associations and others

PHOTOMONTAGE
by Lutz Becker
illustrating the dream of technological power
which guided architects and designers. It
incorporates graphics and photography by
Rodchenko and Rozhkov.

LISSITZKY

art

five Proun studies, about 1920
watercolour, pencil and crayon on paper
a $10\frac{1}{2}$ x $6\frac{1}{2}$ in (27 x 16·8 cm)
b $6\frac{3}{4}$ x $4\frac{3}{8}$ in (17·5 x 11·5 cm)
c 5 x $7\frac{3}{4}$ in (13 x 20 cm)
d $4\frac{7}{8}$ x 10 in (12·8 x 25·7 cm)
e $5\frac{1}{2}$ x $5\frac{1}{2}$ in (14·3 x 14·3 cm) (related to Proun
RVN2, 1923)
(Mrs Donald Ogden Stewart, London)

'Victory over the Sun':
'the plastic forms for the electro-mechanical
performance', Hanover 1923
title-page + ten lithographs in red folder, each
print $15\frac{1}{4}$ x $11\frac{1}{8}$ in (38·3 x 28·5 cm)

a title page
b 'part of the display machinery'
c 'announcer'
d 'sentinel'
e 'frightened people'
f 'globetrotter (in time)'
g 'sportsmen'
h 'brawlers'
i 'old man (head two paces behind)'
j 'gravediggers'
k 'the new man'
(Mrs Walter Neurath, London)

Proun Room, shown in the Grosse Berliner
Kunstausstellung 1923, reconstruction 1971
118 x 118 x 102 in (300 x 300 x 260 cm)
(Stedelijk van Abbemuseum, Eindhoven)

graphics

'Von zwei Quadraten', Berlin 1922
('Story of Two Squares', first published in
Vitebsk, 1920)
cover plus sixteen pages, $8\frac{1}{2}$ x $10\frac{7}{8}$ in (22 x 28 cm)
(Victoria and Albert Museum, London,
and Stedelijk van Abbemuseum, Eindhoven)

'Worden van twe Kwadraten', published by
De Stijl 1922
Dutch edition of the preceding
(Mrs Hannah Höch, Berlin)

'For Reading out Loud', poems by Mayakovsky,
Berlin 1922
(Dr Herbert Spencer, London)

'Six Stories with Happy Endings',
by Ilya Ehrenburg, Berlin 1922
cover and illustrations by Lissitzky
(Victoria and Albert Museum, London)

catalogue cover: '1 Russische
Kunstausstellung', Berlin 1922
('First Russian Art Exhibition')
(Victoria and Albert Museum, London)

"Veshch/Gegenstand/Objet', edited by
Lissitzky and Ehrenburg, Berlin 1922
Nos 1 & 2 (issued as one) and No 3
all published
(British Museum, London)

letterheading for the editorial office of
'Veshch/Gegenstand/Objet', 1922
$11\frac{1}{2}$ x $8\frac{7}{8}$ in (29 x 23 cm)
(Mrs B Gray, Long Wittenham)

'Wendingen' No 11, Amsterdam 1923
cover by Lissitzky
13 x 13 in (33 x 33 cm)
(Norbert Lynton, London)

personal letterheading, c 1924
$10\frac{7}{8}$ x $8\frac{1}{2}$ in (28 x 22 cm)
(Mrs B Gray, Long Wittenham)

'Kunstismen/The Isms of Art' by Lissitzky and
Arp, Zurich Munich & Leipzig 1925
art movements 1924–1914
(Victoria and Albert Museum, and
Chelsea School of Art, London)

'Asnova', Moscow 1926
bulletin of the Association of New Architects
(Stedelijk van Abbemuseum, Eindhoven)

'Das Entfesselte Theater' by Tairov,
Potsdam 1927
('The Theatre Unchained')
cover by Lissitzky
(Victoria and Albert Museum, London)

poster for the Russian Exhibition, Zurich
Kunstgewerbemuseum 1929
exhibition from 24 March to 28 April
(Kunstgewerbemuseum, Zurich)

A&D

design
three watercolours of the 'Kabinet der Abstrakten' in the Landesmuseum, Hanover, 1928
The 'Cabinet of the Abstract Artists' was commissioned by Dr Alexander Dorner in 1926, and constructed in 1927–8, to be the permanent installation of works by avant-garde artists such as Picasso, Léger, Mondrian, Archipenko, Moholy-Nagy and Lissitzky himself. It and its contents were destroyed in 1936
$5\frac{1}{2}$ x 8 in (14·3 x 20·8 cm)
$6\frac{1}{8}$ x $8\frac{1}{8}$ in (16 x 21 cm)
$15\frac{1}{2}$ x $15\frac{3}{4}$ in (39·5 x 40 cm)
(Niedersächsisches Landesmuseum, Hanover)

chair 1930
designed and made for the Russian sections at the International Hygiene Exhibition, Dresden 1930, and the International Fur Trade Exhibition, Leipzig 1930
wood and fibreboard
(reconstructions by John Holloway)

MALEVICH
art
Suprematist Painting (red cross on black circle) c 1916–17
oil on canvas, $23\frac{3}{8}$ x $20\frac{1}{8}$ in (72·5 x 51 cm)
(Stedelijk Museum, Amsterdam)

Suprematist painting (broad white cross on grey) c 1917–18
oil on canvas, $34\frac{5}{8}$ x $26\frac{3}{4}$ in (88 x 68·5 cm)
(Stedelijk Museum, Amsterdam)

Suprematist Composition
pencil on paper, 10 x $7\frac{3}{4}$ in (25·5 x 19·7 cm)
(Annely Juda Fine Art)

Suprematist Composition
pencil on paper, $7\frac{1}{8}$ x $4\frac{3}{4}$ in (18·2 x 11 cm)
(Michael Tollemache Ltd)

Suprematist Composition
pencil on paper, $6\frac{3}{4}$ x $4\frac{5}{8}$ in (17 x 11·7 cm)
(Michael Tollemache Ltd)

Suprematist Composition
pencil on paper $7\frac{1}{8}$ x $4\frac{3}{4}$ in (18·2 x 11 cm)
(Annely Juda Fine Art)

Future planets for earth dwellers, 1924
pencil on paper
(Stedelijk Museum, Amsterdam)

Suprematism, the Supremacy of pure Non-Objective Art, the Phases of its Development, (after 1923)
three-paged MS, ink on paper with watercolour each page 13 x $8\frac{1}{4}$ in (33 x 21 cm)
(Annely Juda Fine Art)

Painting and the Problems of Architecture (the new classical system of architecture), Berlin 1927
three-paged MS, ink on paper with watercolour, each page 13 x $8\frac{1}{4}$ in (33 x 21 cm)
(Annely Juda Fine Art)

MILLER
graphics
'All Roads are Open', 1927
cover by G Miller
(Dr Szymon Bojko, Warsaw)

design
two designs for a drawing table
(Dr Szymon Bojko, Warsaw)

POPOVA
art
Architectonic Composition, c 1917
oil on canvas, 28 x 28 in (71 x 71 cm)
(Wilhelm Hack, Cologne)

RODCHENKO
graphics
slogans from the exhibition '*5 x 5 = 25*', Moscow 1921
signed by Rodchenko and Stepanova
(the exhibition consisted of new works by Rodchenko, Stepanova, Exter, Popova and A Vesnin)
a 'Study the old, create the new'
9 x $10\frac{1}{2}$ in (23 x 27 cm)
b 'The Future is our sole aim'
9 x $13\frac{1}{2}$ in (23 x 36 cm)(Dr Szymon Bojko, Warsaw)

'Pro Eto': anthology of Mayakovsky poems, Moscow 1923
photomontages and layout by Rodchenko
9 x 6 in (22 x 14·6 cm)
(School of Slavonic and East European Studies University of London)

'L'Art Decoratif URSS' Paris and Moscow 1925
catalogue of Soviet contribution to the Decorative Arts Exhibition in Paris
(Victoria and Albert Museum, London)

'The People's Masses', Moscow 1925
cover by Rodchenko
(Dr Szymon Bojko, Warsaw)

'Novy Lef', magazine of the Constructivists,
edited by Mayakovsky 1927–8
covers and layout by Rodchenko
(several issues also reproduce photographs by
Rodchenko)
Nos 4–12
(British Museum, London)

'Dayosh', Moscow 1929
('Give')
cover
(Dr Szymon Bojko, Warsaw)

photomontage: a page from the album
'The First Cavalry'
14½ x 11¾ in (37 x 30 cm)
(Dr Szymon Bojko, Warsaw)

Letterheading for the editorial office of
'Zarubeshom'
('Abroad')
(Dr Szymon Bojko, Warsaw)

SENKIN
graphics
photomontage for 'March of Youth', 1931
7 x 8¼ in (18 x 21 cm)
(Dr Szymon Bojko, Warsaw)

STEPANOVA
design
fabrics and garments designed 1924
a–b two dresses, fabrics printed by Rosemary
Newson at St Albans School of Art, made up by
Ariane Lewis
c a coat, fabric printed by Rosemary Newson at
St Albans School of Art, made up by Ariane
Lewis
d–i six dress fabrics printed by Elspeth Reynolds,
Rodney Moorhouse and Bob Beard at Chelsea
School of Art

TATLIN
art
Corner Relief 1915
reconstruction in wood, metal and wire
31 x 34 x 28 in (79·5 x 26 x 71 cm)
made by Martyn Chalk, 1966–70
(Martyn L Chalk, Kingston upon Hull)

Complex Corner Relief 1915
reconstruction in iron, zinc, aluminium etc
31 x 60 x 30 in (79 x 151 x 75·5 cm)
made by Martyn Chalk, 1966–70
(Martyn L Chalk, Kingston upon Hull)

design
bent-tube chair with moulded rubber seat, c 1927
(reconstruction by Enterprise Metal Co)

TELINGATER
graphics
'Let Kirsanov have the floor'
cover
(Dr Szymon Bojko, Warsaw)

art
GROUP OF PAINTINGS
from the Tretyakov State Museum, Moscow, and
others the avant-garde artists' move 'into the
streets' left the field of art to those artists who
remained closer to naturalism. Their descriptive
and directly communicative work was encouraged by the state as another form of mass
communication, comparable to posters and film

SOVIET DESIGN SINCE 1930
a display to show
more recent developments
in architecture, art and design
in the Soviet Union

Season of Soviet Films
at the National Film Theatres
organised in collaboration with the Arts Council

NFT Two
two programmes, every Monday to Friday afternoon, 2–3 and 3.30–4.30, devoted to the work of Dziga Vertov and specially his Kino-Pravda films

open to the public: free admission to holders of ART IN REVOLUTION exhibition ticket

NFT One
twenty programmes, 25 February to 31 March, listed below
members only

Kino Pravda
Thu 25 Feb   6.15 8.30
Vertov's *Cinema-Truth* series, a revolutionary film-journal about life in the Soviet Union, began on 21 May 1922, and lasted through twenty-three amazing editions. Lively, informative and inventive, the series gave Vertov the chance to develop his editing theories into the most artistic newsreels ever made. Though most of the footage was shot by his 'correspondents', it was Vertov and his assistant Yelizaveta Svilova who edited the film into something startlingly new. USSR 1922–25. Dir Dziga Vertov.

The Extraordinary Adventures of Mr West in the Land of the Bolsheviks
By the Law
Fri 26 Feb   6.15 8.30   **Mon 1 Mar**   6.15 8.30
Lev Kuleshov, the master theorist behind the development of the Soviet cinema in the 1920s, was also one of its most brilliant film-makers. *The Extraordinary Adventures of Mr West in the Land of the Bolsheviks* (1924), a dazzling comedy satirising Western concepts of 'Red Russia', will be shown at both 6.15 performances. *By the Law* (1926), an amazing Alaskan Western based on a Jack London story and mathematically intense in every gesture, will be shown at both 8.30 performances. A rare opportunity to re-discover one of the great masters of world cinema.

Strike
Fri 26 Feb   11.00
Eisenstein's first film is a complex and brilliant story about the repression of a strike in Russia in about 1912. An enormously rich film visually and technically, it is possibly the most complete representation of the ideas of the Constructivist art movement. Symbolistic, surrealistic, a mosaic of stunning images, it is highly theatrical in the best sense and contains some of the most original film sequences ever made. USSR 1924

Dir Sergei Eisenstein. Photographed by Eduard Tissé. With Maxim Shtraukh, Grigori Alexandrov, Mikhail Gomorov.

Battleship Potemkin
Sat 27 Feb   4.00 6.15 8.30   **Public**
Like Leonardo's Gioconda, *Potemkin* suffers from being almost too well-known. And yet it is still extraordinarily powerful, all of the fervour of revolutionary Russia coalescing into one of the most brilliant aesthetic experiences of the cinema in the hands of a twenty-seven-year-old youth who had previously directed only one film. USSR 1925 Dir Sergei Eisenstein. Photographed by Eduard Tissé.

Kino-Glas
Stride, Soviet!
Tue 2 Mar   6.15 8.30
Kino-Eye (1924) was Dziga Vertov's first feature-length demonstration of his theories of montage and filming 'life as it is'. His techniques included everything from hidden cameras to living with the people he filmed. *Stride, Soviet!* (1926) is a symphonic film-poem to the Soviet worker all over the USSR at the time of the reconstruction. In it Vertov elaborated the ideas of Constructivism by integrating his subtitles through typography into the film almost like photo-montage.

Aelita
His Call
Thu 4 Mar   6.15 8.45
Yakov Protazanov's *Aelita* (1924) is the most memorable achievement of the ideas of Constructivism in film sets (designed by Alexandra Exter and Isaac Rabinovich). The story concerns a young Russian who lands on Mars and starts a revolution. *His Call* (1925) is a realistic agitational film about the people of a small village and the effect that the revolution and the years leading up to the death of Lenin has on them.

The End of the Dynasty Romanov
The Great Way
Fri 5 Mar 6.15 8.30
Esther Shub was perhaps even more sensitive than Vertov to the emotional effects that could be obtained by juxtaposing bits of newsreel. Her *Romanov* compilation of newsreel material achieves effects from pathos to grandeur simply by putting historical fragments concerning the Tsar into an artistic whole. In the same year (1927) she put together another extraordinary compilation, *The Great Way*, about the ten years after the 1917 Revolution.

Mother
Sat 6 Mar 4.00 6.15 8.30 **Public**
Pudovkin's ideas of editing differed greatly from Eisenstein but the cinematic result of his theories was equally exciting as the continuing effectiveness of *Mother* so remarkably demonstrates. The story, based on Gorky, concerns the very contemporary idea of the radicalisation of a mother through her son's revolutionary activities in 1905 Russia. USSR 1926 Dir V I Pudovkin. With Vera Baranovskaya, Nikolai Batalov.

A Sixth of the Earth
The Eleventh
Mon 8 Mar 6.15 8.30
A Sixth of the World (1926) is Vertov's lyrical cinema-poem to the vast expanses of the Soviet Union, grand, complicated, exotic and hugely popular. His cameramen ranged over all the Soviet regions and the film had a strong influence on the Western documentary movement. *The Eleventh* is the eleventh year of the USSR and shows the victories of the socialist society and its industries.

The End of St Petersburg
Wed 10 Mar 6.15 8.45 **Fri 12 Mar** 11.15
A contemporary critic called this pictorial masterpiece a 'film of images' and possibly the influence of the poet Alexander Blok helped to make it the most deliberately symbolistic of Pudovkin's films. It is the visually breathtaking but highly dramatic reconstruction of events in St Petersburg which led up to the 1917 Revolution. The story follows a young peasant from 1914 through the war years to the Revolution that ended St Petersburg and created Leningrad. USSR 1927 Dir V I Uudovkin. With Vera Baranovaskaya, A Christiakov.

Spring
The Forty-First
Thu 11 Mar 6.15 8.30
A double programme starting with Mikhail Kaufman's (Vertov's cameraman brother) documentary film-poem *Spring* (1930), which strongly influenced the British documentary movement. Yakov Protazanov's 1927 *The Forty-First* (re-made in 1956 by Chukhrai) is the story of a Red Army girl soldier who falls in love with a White Guard officer but overcomes her emotions and shoots him as her forty-first enemy victim.

Storm Over Asia
Fri 12 Mar 6.00 8.45
The lyricism of this exotic Pudovkin film, also known under the title of *The Heir to Genghis Khan*, is an astonishing flowering of Kuleshov's editing ideas, 'a glittering flow of polished, glossy images that could leave breathless a spectator accustomed to the "normal" film' (Jay Leyda). The villains of the film are the British who capture a young Mongol trapper in the civil war days of 1920 in Mongolia and try to use him as a puppet leader when they discover his ancestry. USSR 1928 Dir V I Pudovkin. With Valeri Inhizhinov.

October
Sat 13 Mar 3.00 6.00 9.00
Tue 16 Mar 6.00 9.00
Eisenstein's reconstruction of the events of the Russian Revolution of 1917, again photographed by Eduard Tissé, has an epic air of objectivity and newsreel accuracy but its power is due to Eisenstein's own personal attitudes and views of the Revolution and his montage technique. What he calls 'intellectual dynamism' infuses the film with a vitality that surpasses mere history. USSR 1928 Dir Sergei Eisenstein and Grigori Alexandrov.

The Man with the Movie Camera
Mon 15 Mar 6.15 8.30

Vertov's best-known film is one of the most fascinating exercises in film editing ever assembled as well as being one of the most delightful. The real hero of the film is the camera which shares honours with cameraman Mikhail Kaufman in a puckish look at life in the Soviet Union and the techniques of film-making itself. Filled with 'trick' effects of super-imposition, changing camera speeds and unexpected points of view, it delights, teaches and demonstrates Vertov's theories of cinema all at the same time. Plus extracts from Vertov's 1921 *Cinema-Week* series. USSR 1928 Dir Dziga Vertov.

The General Line
Thu 18 Mar 6.15 8.30 **Fri 19 Mar** 11.00

Eisenstein's last silent film, also known as *Old and New*, is one of the most important films in the history of editing, an advance in a different direction from *October*, from 'intellectual' to 'sensual' montage. The story is concerned with the conflict between old and new styles of farming but the structure is built harmonically out of emotional image-music, what the director later defined as 'tonal montage'. USSR 1929 Dir Sergei Eisenstein and Grigori Alexandrov.

Zvenigora
Mon 22 Mar 6.15 8.30

Dovzhenko's astonishing film, once called 'an Ukrainian *Intolerance*', led Eisenstein and Pudovkin to hail the arrival of a new director of genius. The story uses Zvenigora, a legendary treasure hill, as the central symbol of an anthology of legends but it is the arrival of socialism which actually reveals the hidden treasures of the earth. The wealth of technical experiments and cinematic surprises make *Zvenigora* comparable to *Strike*. USSR 1928 Dir Alexander Dovzhenko.

Arsenal
Wed 24 Mar 6.15 8.30

'*Arsenal* is completely a political film,' says Dovzhenko of this epic-poem about the Ukraine and the bloody repression of a workers' rebellion in a Kiev munitions factory in January 1918. Eisenstein hailed the film for its 'liberation of the whole action from the definitions of time and space' and many critics feel that Dovzhenko was the first to maturely coalesce all the theories of the great Soviet film-makers. USSR 1929 Dir Alexander Dovzhenko.

Three Songs of Lenin
Fri 26 Mar 6.15 8.30

Generally considered Vertov's masterpiece and his last important film, *Three Songs of Lenin* is primarily concerned with the effect Lenin's life and teaching has had on the women of central Asia. The film is structured about three Uzbekistan folksongs about Lenin and its moving lyricism shows Vertov in tight control of his virtuoso skills in editing sound and pictures. USSR 1934 Dir Dziga Vertov.

Sickle and Hammer
Turksib
Mon 29 Mar 6.15 9.00

Vladimir Gardin gave Pudovkin his start in the cinema with *Sickle and Hammer* (1921) for which he was both assistant director and leading man. Victor Turin's *Turksib* (1929) is the story of the building of the Turkestan-Siberian railway, an impressionist documentary which influenced the British documentary school perhaps as much as any other film. A landmark of the genre, it retains an amazing freshness and vitality.

Donbas Symphony
Wed 31 Mar 6.15 8.30

Vertov's first sound film is also called *Symphony of the Don Basin*, a most accurate description of what is almost *musique concrète* in advance of its time. Ostensibly a film about the enthusiasm of the miners in the Don coal basin fulfilling their five-year plan, it is really a virtuoso demonstration of Vertov's montage theories applied to sound. Charles Chaplin called it 'one of the finest symphonies I've ever heard'. USSR 1930 Dir Dziga Vertov.

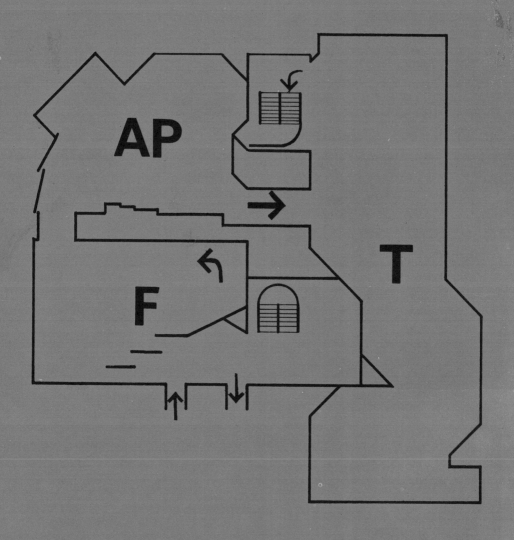

First Floor

F   documentary composite film

AP   agit-prop: posters and other
        mass communication graphics

T   theatre design